D1542894

Merie Tales
of the Mad Men of Gotam

_____

*and*

The History of Tom Thumbe

*The Renaissance English Text Society*

*Editorial Committee*

R. C. Bald, *Chairman*
W. A. Ringler, Jr.
M. A. Shaaber

dir
prepaid

DISCARDED

Mad men of Gotham

828·3          M178 me

PR
973
K3
1965

A. B. of Phisike Doctour,

# Merie Tales
# of the Mad Men of Gotam

*Edited by Stanley J. Kahrl*

---

*and*

R. I.,

# The History of Tom Thumbe

*Edited by Curt F. Bühler*

*Northwestern University Press, Evanston, Illinois*

*for The Renaissance English Text Society*
*1965*

*Copyright © 1965 by Northwestern University Press*
*Library of Congress Catalog Card Number: 64–14422*
*Printed in the United States of America*

*Design by William A. Seabright*

# Contents

## Merie Tales of the Mad Men of Gotam

## The History of Tom Thumbe

A. B. of Phisike Doctour,

# Merie Tales
# of the Mad Men of Gotam

*Edited by Stanley J. Kahrl*

# Introduction

The earliest text heretofore available of *The Merry Tales of the Mad Men of Gotham* is the relatively late edition published in 1630 by Michael Sparke which has been reprinted in the third volume of W. C. Hazlitt's *Old English Jest-Books* (1864). Earlier editions are known to have existed. The earliest entry in the Stationers' Register is an assignment of copies belonging to the late Hugh Jackson to another publisher of the same name on 22 July 1616.[1] Thomas Warton, in a footnote to his discussion of the purported author, Andrew Boorde, stated that a duodecimo edition existed, printed by "Henry Wikes," about 1568.[2] In *Notices of Popular English Histories*,[3] J. O.

---

1. Edward Arber, *A Transcript of the Registers of the Company of Stationers of London* (London, 1875), III, 593 (hereafter referred to as Arber). See also *Records of the Court of the Stationers' Company 1602 to 1640*, ed. W. A. Jackson (London, 1957), pp. 87–88.

2. *History of English Poetry* (London, 1781), III, 73. Warton himself had seen only Sparke's edition.

3. (London, 1848), pp. 72–73.

Halliwell described another early edition, printed by Thomas Colwell, no date, black letter, which he dated 1556–1566. A unique copy of this edition has now come into the possession of the Harvard College Library and is the basis of the present reprint. After the *Hundred Merry Tales and Mery Tales, Witti Questions, and Quicke Answeres,* this is certainly one of the earliest sixteenth-century collections of jests, and the first to use the opening geographic reference of the medieval *exempla* as an organizing device. Several of the tales are of considerable antiquity, dating in some cases from the twelfth century. The best known is the first tale, the motif of which is the basis of a considerable section of the "First Shepherds' Play" of the Towneley cycle.

The Harvard copy is bound in a late-seventeenth-century binding, together with a copy of *Mery Tales, Witti Questions, and Quicke Answeres,* dated 1567,[4] and a translation of one of Erasmus' *Colloquia,* dated 1557. The title page of Colwell's edition reads, in black letter:

Merie Tales of | the mad men of | Gotam. | Gathered to gether by A. B. | of Phisike Doc- | tour. | [Printer's device, McKerrow no. 68.]

The lower right-hand corner is slightly torn. The colophon (C4) reads, in black letter, "Imprinted at London in Fletstret, be- | neath thf [sic] Conduit, at the signe

---

4. The edition of *Mery Tales, Witti Questions, and Quicke Answeres* was printed by H. Wykes. If Warton saw this particular volume, the reference to "Wikes" as printer of *The Merry Tales* could be accounted for. No other evidence that Wykes printed *The Merry Tales* is known.

of | S. Iohn Euangelist, by | Thomas Colwell." This is followed on C4$^v$ by the same printer's device (St. John, seated, on the island of Patmos) as that on the title page; Colwell had inherited it from Robert Wyer, whose shop he had taken over about 1560. In Colwell's edition the signatures run A-B$^8$C$^4$ with A2 missigned B2; A1$^v$ is blank. The running title, omitted on A2 and on C3 where it is replaced by the chapter title, is "Certaine merie tales | of the mad men of Gotam." There are no errors in catchwords, but there are some spelling variations: A3$^v$ wolde/ wold, A4 his/ hys, A5$^v$ sayd/ sayde, A6$^v$ against/ againste, A7$^v$ way [?]/ waye, B4 pull/ pul, C3 druncke/ drunck.

The date of printing is difficult to determine precisely. Colwell used Wyer's device on at least three other occasions between 1565 (?) and 1571 (?).[5] The block was still usable in 1578 when Hugh Jackson employed it. The edition must be later than 1563, when Colwell moved to the shop in Fleet Street beneath the Conduit,[6] and of course it must be earlier than his death about 1575. There is very little basis for a guess about how long after 1563 the book was published. By 1565 Colwell had published all the copies he is known to have inherited from Wyer; if he also inherited *The Merry Tales*, which Wyer may have published along with other works of Boorde's which he undoubtedly put into print, presumably Col-

---

5. *Printers' and Publishers' Devices . . . 1485–1640*, ed. R. B. McKerrow (London, 1913), p. 24.

6. *Dictionary of Printers . . . 1557–1640*, ed. R. B. McKerrow (London, 1910), p. 74.

well would have reissued it about the same time. The earliest sixteenth-century allusion to the tales occurs about 1577 in the *Comedy of Misogonus*,[7] but this proves nothing if the Gothamites were proverbial fools. A date of c. 1565 seems most appropriate.

Down to the middle of the eighteenth century every title page of *The Merry Tales* follows Colwell in ascribing the book to "A.B. of Phisike Doctour." Until F. J. Furnivall's animadversions on the subject,[8] these initials were regarded as those of Andrew Boorde (or Borde). The earliest identification was made by Anthony à Wood in his *Athenae Oxonienses*, where, in discussing Boorde's writings, he lists

> The Merry Tales of the Mad Men of Gotham. Printed at London in the time of K. Hen. 8, in whose reign and after it was accounted a book full of wit and mirth by scholars and gentlemen. Afterwards being often printed, is now sold only on the stalls of ballad singers.[9]

As Furnivall's sole basis for discrediting Wood's ascription was a feeling that *The Merry Tales* did not accord with Boorde's other writings, his opinion need not be given great weight. As a preservative of good health, Boorde several times prescribed "laudable myrth," [10]

---

7. See J. E. Field, *The Myth of the Pent Cuckoo* (London, 1913), p. 14.

8. See *Andrew Boorde's Introduction and Dyetary with Barnes in the Defence of the Berde*, ed. F. J. Furnivall (London, 1870, E.E.T.S., E.S. x), p. 30.

9. *Athenae Oxonienses* (London, 1691–1692), I, 172. In a footnote, Wood refers to Sparke's edition of 1630.

10. See particularly Furnivall's text of the *Dyetary*, pp. 246, 248, and 300.

which "is, one man or one neyghboure to be mery
with an other, with honesty and vertue, without swer-
yng and sclaunderyng, and rybaldry speaking." [11] The
character of *The Merry Tales* accords well with such a
definition. Boorde did not simply prescribe mirth, however. In the preface to the 1542 edition of the *Dyetary
of Health*, dedicated to Thomas, Duke of Norfolk, Boorde
confesses that if "dyuers tymes in my wrytynges I do
wryte wordes of myrth/truely it is for no other in-
tencyon but to make your grace mery,—for myrth is one
of the chefest thynges of Physycke, the which doth ad-
uertyse euery man to be mery." [12] In addition to the
evidence provided by this professed interest in mirth,
further support for Boorde's authorship derives from the
appearance of a more than accidental interest in the Scottish dialectal words "sewe" and "gryce" ("sow" and
"piglet") in both the *Introduction to Knowledge* [13] and the
eighteenth of *The Merry Tales*. The exceptional spelling
*keyming* (p. 11) rather than *kemming* or *kembing*, is also
found in Boorde's *Breviary*, quoted by Furnivall, p. 95.
Finally, the fact that the first publisher of Boorde's
*Dyetary of Health*, Robert Wyer,[14] was Colwell's prede-

---

11. Boorde's *Breviary*, quoted by Furnivall, p. 88.

12. Furnivall, p. 228.

13. Furnivall, p. 138.

14. Wyer published the first two chapters of the *Dyetary of helth* as *The boke for
to lerne a man to be wyse in buyldyng of his howse for the helth of body* (STC 3373)
c. 1540, and the complete *Dyetary of helth* itself c. 1542 (STC 3379). According
to the notes of Professor W. A. Jackson for the revised STC, Wyer also
published a second edition c. 1545. Professor Jackson lists this as STC 3379
and the earlier edition c. 1542 as 3378.5.

cessor, from whom Colwell acquired his shop, his printing equipment, and some of his copies, suggests that if
*The Merry Tales* was published during Boorde's lifetime,
as Wood says, it may have been published by Wyer, and
Wyer's publication of it would account for Colwell's
possession of the copy. As Colwell was not out of his ap-
prenticeship till 1560, he must have procured the copy
from another source than the author (who had died in
1549), most likely from a source in the book trade and
therefore possibly from Wyer or his estate. Wyer's con-
nection with both Boorde and Colwell makes him the
most likely link between Colwell and *The Merry Tales*.
This link is at least consistent with Boorde's authorship
of *The Merry Tales*, if no very strong proof of it. This
possibility, however, when taken together with Boorde's
expressed interest in mirth and his use of the Scottish dialectal words in the *Introduction to Knowledge*, would seem
to strengthen Wood's ascription. The (highly improb-
able) attribution in 1626 of *The first and best part of Scog-
gins jests* (STC 21852) to Boorde proves at least that,
seventy-five years after his death, he had some reputation
as a composer of jests. As this book was published by
Francis Williams, in 1626 the owner of the copyright of
*The Merry Tales*, perhaps Williams thought that Boorde
was the A.B. of his *Merry Tales*.

Though a precise date of composition cannot be determined, there are a few internal indications of a time as
early as the reign of Henry VIII, during the last decade
of which most of Boorde's works seem to have been written and were undoubtedly first published. References to
the Pater Noster and the mass, shrift and penance, cros-
sing oneself against the devil and the emphasis on fasting

point to a period of Catholic observances. In the first tale both shepherds swear "by the masse" (in later editions the oaths are omitted). In general, the language seems to agree well enough with a date of composition not long after, or even somewhat before, 1540. A few words in the tales seem to have become obsolete or obsolescent not long after this date. "Caste theyr heads together" (p. 6) is illustrated by the *OED* only from Skelton's *Magnyfycence* (1526). The adverb *still* as used at p. 4 ("without change of place"), except with *stand* or *sit*, is not attested by the *OED* after the middle of the century. The examples of *faynded* (p. 10) in the *OED* are medieval. Of "thus many" (p. 6) the *OED* gives but one example dated 1531. "By the way" (p. 9), meaning "by the road-side," seems to have become uncommon by the middle of the sixteenth century and was apparently not understood by the reviser of the 1630 edition, who substituted "upon the highway." This evidence, so far as it goes, supports a date of composition during Boorde's lifetime.

As there is some external evidence suggesting that *The Merry Tales* was printed during the presumed author's lifetime and that Colwell's edition was not the first, it would be desirable, if possible, to find internal evidence of composition either from printed copy or from manuscript. Unfortunately such evidence is not forthcoming. The only conspicuous typographical anomaly in the text of Colwell's edition is sig. B2$^r$, which is two lines longer than other pages. At the foot of the page there is some crowding since the signature and the catchword form one line of type with a few words of the text. Perhaps something accidentally omitted was added to sig. B2$^r$

after the forme containing the verso page had been made ready or printed (or even earlier if the printer was too lazy to make a drastic change). It may have been a simple haplography: the last sentence on B2ʳ and the first on B2ᵛ begin with the same words, "And when he." Conceivably such an error could occur in setting type from either a manuscript or printed copy. The most that can be said is that there appears to be nothing in the typographical make-up of the book that is inconsistent with its being a reprint.

The editions later than Colwell's (see the list which follows) do not concern us here. They testify to the enduring popularity of *The Merry Tales* and exemplify the usual history of perennial favorites like it. Speaking of reprints of long-lived works of prose fiction in the seventeenth century, Professor Mish says:

> The typical pattern is this: an earlier text is rewritten to make the language contemporary; a sequel or continuation is provided; and finally abridgments of the original are made. Few books show this process in all three stages, but it may be thought of as the ideal "full treatment" of a popular story. . . . To judge from their looks, they were put together as cheaply as could be to reach a market which would neither spend much for books nor indeed have much money to spend in any case.[15]

The reprints of *The Merry Tales* tally with this description. They are cheaply printed in black letter; they regu-

---

15. Charles C. Mish, "Best Sellers in Seventeenth-century Fiction," *PBSA*, XLVII (1953), 371.

larly revise the text so as to eliminate archaism. A sequel
was entered in the Stationers' Register by John Harrison
on 13 April 1637 ("the second part of the wise men of
Gotham"),[16] but if it was printed no copy has survived.
Obviously a certain number of readers and the publishers
who catered for them cherished *The Merry Tales* for many
years.

## List of Editions

[1]   c. 1565. Colwell's edition (see p. x). HD.[17]

[2]   c. 1568. The following note, alluded to on page
      ix, appears in Thomas Warton's *History of
      English Poetry* (London, 1781), III, 73. "There
      is an edition in duodecimo by Henry Wikes,
      without date, but about 1568, entitled, *Merie
      Tales of the madmen of Gotam, gathered together by
      A.B. of physicke doctour.* The oldest I have seen,
      is London, 1630, 12mo." In his edition of the
      *History* (London, 1871), IV, 69, W. C. Hazlitt
      adds: "[The oldest] edition now traceable is
      that of 1630, mentioned by Warton, and re-
      printed in *Old English Jest-Books*, vol. iii. The

---

16. Arber, IV, 381.

17. Harvard College Library. Other libraries referred to are the Bodleian
Library (O) and the British Museum (L).

edition by Wykes is unknown; but Mr. Halliwell, in his *Popular English Histories*, p. 71,
refers to one by Thomas Colwell."

[3]  1613. "Merie Tales of the Mad Men of Gotham.
London, 1613, 12mo. Harleian Cat." W. C.
Hazlitt, *Hand-book of the Popular, Poetical, and
Dramatic Literature of Great Britain* (London,
1867), p. 47.

[4]  1619. The following entry in the court book of
the Stationers' Company dated 3 May 1619 is
the only evidence of an edition published
shortly before that time: "It is ordered that
mr Eld and m$^r$ Flesher shall pay to mr [Roger]
Jackson vj$^s$ viij$^d$ for imprynting the booke
called Madmen of Gotam which was formerly
entred to the said mr Jackson" (*Records of the
Court of the Stationers' Company 1602 to 1640*, ed.
W. A. Jackson [London, 1957], p. 110). "The
merry tales of the mad men of Gottam" is one
of a list of books "Assigned ouer to Henry Bell
by Raphe Blower" on 26 August 1617 (Arber,
III, 613), but this title was subsequently
crossed out and "Entered to master fflesher"
written opposite it in the margin. Hence, no
doubt, Flesher's claim. But how Blower considered that he had the right to sell the copy
defies explanation.

[5]  1630. THE | MERRY TALES | OF THE
MAD MEN | OF *GOTTAM* | – | Gath-

ered together by *AB.* of Physicke Docto [18] |
[cut depicting a man inside a stylized fence
holding a stick and facing a bird in a tree to
his right] | Printed at London by B.A[lsop].
and T.F[awcet]. for *Micha* [18] | Sparke, dwel-
ling in *Greene Arbor* at the signe of the *Blue-
Bible*. 1630. A⁸B⁴. O.

The publication of this edition by Sparke
raises questions. Colwell's copyrights passed
into the hands of Hugh Jackson, who married
his widow; Jackson republished a number of
them and at his death the Stationers' Company
assigned certain ones, including *The Merry
Tales*, to Roger Jackson (no relation).[19] Roger
Jackson's widow in turn transferred *The Merry
Tales*, with other copies, to Francis Williams
on 16 January 1626.[20] Apparently Williams
did not exercise his right to issue *The Merry
Tales*, but on 29 June 1630 he sold it to John
Harrison.[21] At the time of Sparke's edition,
therefore, the copyright belonged to either
Williams or Harrison and presumably Sparke
had no claim to it. As there is no record of any
punitive action against Sparke, perhaps he
published *The Merry Tales* under a private con-

---

18. The edge of the page is missing here.

19. See note 1.

20. Arber, IV, 149.

21. *Ibid.*, 237.

tract with the copyright owner. Sparke's woodcut (see p. xxv), which illustrates the third tale, was apparently commissioned specifically for *The Merry Tales*. Sparke's choice of the third tale for purposes of illustration is particularly interesting in view of the survival to this day of the name "Cuckoo Bush" for a point of land near Gotham, Notts., supposedly localizing the spot at which the cuckoo was hedged. A later imitation of Sparke's design, where the man and bird are reversed, occurs on the title page of an edition printed for Coniers and Deacon (see number 8 below), now in the British Museum. Another version appears in the various editions printed by William and Cluer Dicey in London during the eighteenth century, and is reproduced in John Ashton's *Chapbooks of the Eighteenth Century* (London, 1882), p. 276. One of the latest versions is reproduced by Stapleton (*All about the Merry Tales of Gotham* [Nottingham, 1910], on p. 79).

[6]    1650. "Merie Tales of the Mad Men of Gotham. Lond., 1650. 8vo. *Bodleian* (Wood). In the Catalogue of Wood's Coll., but mislaid." W. C. Hazlitt, *Hand-book*, p. 47.

[7]    1684–1686. "The Merry Tales of the Mad-Men of Gotham . . . Printed for J. Clarke, W. Thackeray, and T. Passinger. 8°, A-B⁴ in eights. Pepysian." W. C. Hazlitt, *Collections and Notes 1867–1876* (London, 1876), I, 477.

The partnership of Clarke, Thackeray, and Passinger for the publication of ballads is limited by Cyprian Blagden ("Notes on the Ballad Market," *Studies in Bibliography*, VI [1954], 172) to the years 1684–1686 (the termini are the death of John Wright, a former member of the syndicate, in October 1684, and that of Clarke, who made his will on 16 August 1686). Presumably they published *The Merry Tales* during this span of time.

[8]  [1690?]. The | Merry Tales | of | The Mad-Men of *Gotam* | — | By *A.B.* Doctor of Physick. | [cut depicting man inside wattled fence holding stick facing bird in tree to his left: man saying "Coocou," bird, "Gotam"][22] | Printed by J.R. for G. Coniers, at the Golden-Ring, | on Ludgate-Hill, and J. Deacon, at the Angel in Guilt-Spur-Street without Newgate. n.d. 12mo., 12 leaves, black letter. L. Hazlitt, *Hand-book*, p. 47. Wing, STC 1641–1700, No. B3749 gives this title page as "by J.R. for G. Conters & J. Dacon."

In the period of the chapbooks, it is no longer feasible to trace all subsequent editions of *The Merry Tales*. Drawing for the most part on the catalogue of the British Museum and the Harvard College Library collection of chapbooks brought together by George Lyman Kittredge, I

---

22. Reproduced in J. P. Collier, *Roxburghe Ballads* (London, 1847), p. 126.

have been able to identify twenty-one separate editions of *The Merry Tales* between the edition of 1701 and Hazlitt's edition of 1864. There were undoubtedly more, for *The Merry Tales of the Mad Men of Gotham* remained popular well into the nineteenth century.

The following text is set up from the unique Harvard College Library copy of the undated edition printed by Thomas Colwell c. 1565. Abbreviations (&, y$^e$, y$^t$, w$^t$, and macron over vowel) have been expanded silently, and "long s" has been printed "s"; otherwise the copy text has been reproduced *literatim*, except for the correction of manifest errors that are noted at the foot of the page. The original, which is printed throughout in black letter (except for the fourth line of the title page and initial large capitals), is here printed in roman.

Woodcut on title page of Sparke's 1630 edition
*Courtesy of the Library of Harvard University*

# THE
# MERRY TALES
## OF THE MAD-MEN
### OF GOTTAM.

Gathered together by *A B.* of Physicke Docto

Printed at London by *B. A.* and *T. F.* for *Micha*
*Sparke*, dwelling in *Greene Arbor* at the signe of
the *Blue-Bible*, 1630.

2 L 79
Art (1)
25

Title page of Colwell's edition, c. 1565.
*Courtesy of the Library of Harvard University*

# Merie Tales of

## the mad men of Gotam.

Gathered to gether by A. B.

of Phisike Doctour.

Initial letter is facsimile (retouched) from the Library
of Harvard University

# ℭ Here beginneth certain
## merie tales of the mad men
## of Gotam.


### ¶ The first tale.

Heare was two men of Gotam, and the one was goyng to the market to Nottyngham to buye sheepe and the other dyd come from the Market, and bothe met together vppon Nottingham brydge. Well met said the one to the other. Whether be you going (sayde hee that came from Nottyngeham, to hym that wente to Nottingeham.) Marye sayde he that
10 wente to Nottyngham, I goe to the market to buye sheepe. | Buye sheepe saide the other? and whyche waye wylte thou brynge them? Marye sayde the other, I wyll brynge them ouer thys bridge. By Robyn hoode sayd he that cam from Nottingham, but thou shalte not. By Mayde Maryon sayde he that wente to the market but I wyll. Thou shalte not sayde the other. I wyll sayde the other. Ter here, sayd the one. Showe theare, sayde the other. They
20 beat theyr staues agaynste the grounde, one agaynste the other, as theare had bene a hun-

dred sheepe betwixt them. Holde in theare sayde
the one. Beware of leapyng ouer the brydge of my
sheepe sayd the other, I care not said the other, they
shal not come thys waye by the masse. By the masse
sayde the other, but they | shall. Then sayde the      [A3
other, and thou make muche to doe, I wyll put my
fynger in thy mouthe. A turde thou wilte, saide the
other. And as they weare at thys contencyon, another man of Gotam dyd come from the market
10  wyth a sacke of meale vppon an horse. And seyng
and hearing his neyghboures at stryfe, for sheepe,
and none betwixt them said a fooles will you neuer
learne wyt. Helpe me saide hee that had the meale,
and laye my sacke vppon my shulder, they dyd so.
And he went to the one side of the bridge, and vn-
losed the mouth of the sacke, and did shake oute
all hys meale into the ryuer, now neyghbour sayde
this man, howe much meale is theare in my sacke
nowe, marye theare is none at all sayde they, |
20  Now by my faythe sayd he euen as muche witte is in   [A3ᵛ
youre twoo headdes, to stryue for that thyng which
ye haue not.
Which was the wisest of al these three persons?
Iudge you.


❡ The ii. tale.


30  THeare was a man of Gotam dyd ryde to thee mar-
     ket wyth twoo bussheles of wheate, and by-
cause hys horse shoulde not beare heauye, hee ca-

---

4 not] uot C.        19 none] noue C.

ryed hys corne vppon hys owne necke, and dyd
ryde vppon hys horse, because hys horse shoulde
not cary no heauy burthen.

### ¶ The iii. tale.

ON a time the men of Gotam, | wold haue   [A4
pynned the Cockow, that she should sing all
the yeare and in the myddest of the towne they dyd
make a hedge (round in compas,) and they had got
a Cocow, and put her in it and sayde, singe here all
the yeare, and thou shalte lacke neyther meate nor
drincke. The Cocow as soone as shee was set wyth
in the hedge, flew her waye. A vengeaunce on her
sayde they, we made not our hedge high ynough.

### ¶ The iiii. tale.

THere was a man of Gotam the which went to the
market to Nottingham to sell cheese. And as hee
was goynge downe the hyll to Nottingham brydge,
one of hys cheeses dyd fall out of | hys poake, and   [A4ᵛ
did runne downe the hyl. A horsons said the felow,
can you runne to the market alone I will sende the
one after the other of you. He layde downe hys
poake, and tooke the cheeses, and dyd trundle them
downe the hyll one after another: and some ran into
one busshe, and some into another. And at the laste

he sayde I charge you all meete me in the market
place. When the fellowe dyd come into the market
place to meete hys cheeses, hee dyd tarie tyll the
market was almoste done. Then he went about, and
dyd inquyre of hys neighboures, and other men if
they did see his cheeses come to the market? Who
shoulde bringe them? sayd one of the market men.
Marye them selues sayd the fellow, they knew |
the way well ynoughe. He taryed still tyll it was      [A5
10    nyght. At nyghte he said a vengeaunce on them al.
I dyd feare to see that my cheeses dyd runne so faste,
that they runne beyonde the market: I am sure that
they be almoste now at Yorke. He hyred a horse to
ryde after to Yorke to seeke hys cheeses wheare they
weare not. But to thys daye, no man coulde tell
hym of hys cheeses.


¶ The v. tale.

20


THeare was a man of Gotam and he did buy at
   Nottyngeham a Trefete (or a Brandyron.) And
as he was going home, his shoulder dyd ake: |
And hee dyd set downe hys Trefete, and see that it      [A5ᵛ
had thre feete sayde, a horsen, haste thou three
feete, and I but two, thou shalte beare me home if
thou wilte, and dyd syt downe on the trefete and
sayd, beare me as long as I haue borne the, for if
30    thou do not, thou shalt stand still for mee. The

---

13 hyred] byred C.

man of Gotam dyd see that hys Trefete wolde not goe further, stand styll sayd he in the Mares name, and folowe mee if thou wylte, I wyll tell thee the ryghte waye to my house. Whan he did com home to his house his wife sayd, where is my Brandiron or trefete. The man sayde he hath three legges, and I haue but two legges, and I dyd teach hym the way to my house, let hym come home if hee wyll. Wheare lefte ye the Trefete | sayde the wyfe? At [A6 Gotam hyll, sayde the man. The wife did run and fetch home hir trefete, or else she had lost it.


## ¶ The vi tale.


THeare dwelt a smith in Gotam, the whych had a Waspes nest in the straw in the ende of his Forge. Theare dyd come one of hys neyghboures to haue hys horse shooed, and the waspes weare so busye that the fellow was stong, with a waspe. He beyng angrye sayde, art thou worthy to keepe a Forge, to haue men stunge here wythe Waspes? O neygh-boure sayde the smythe, be content. I wyll put them from theyr neste bye and bye. He tooke a Coulter and heated it in hys | Forge glowyng [A6ᵛ hote, and thruste it into the strawe in the ende of hys Forge. And so he dyd set hys Forge a fyre, and dyd burne it vppe. Than sayde the Smythe. I tolde thee that I woulde fyre them furth of theyr nestes.

---

5 to] tq C.        7 haue] hane C.

### ¶ The vii. tale.

WHen that good Frydaye was come, the men of
Gotam dyd caste theyr heads together what
they shuld doe with theyr whyte hearyng, and
10   theyr red hearyng, and their sprottes, and salt
fyshe. One consulted with the other, and agreed
that all such fysh should be cast into their pond or
poole (the whiche was in the myddle of theyr   [A7
towne,) that it myghte increase | againste the
nexte yeare. Euerye man that had any fishe lefte,
dyd cast it into the poole, the one sayd I haue thus
manye whyte hearinges, the other sayde, I haue
thus many sprots, another sayde I haue thus many
red hearings, the other said I haue thus much salte
20   fyshe. Let all go together in to the poole or pond,
and we shall fare like Lordes next lent. At the be-
ginninge of the next lent, folowinge, the men dyd
drawe theyr ponde to haue theyr fyshe: and there
was nothing but a great Ele.
   (A sayde they all) a myschiefe on this Ele, for he
hathe eate vp all our fyshe. What shal we do wyth
hym sayde the one to the other. Kill hym said another. Chop him al to peces said another. Nay not
so said other, let vs drowne him: be it sayd all.
30   | They wente to another poole or pond by, and dyd   [A7ᵛ
cast in the Eele into the water. Lye theare sayde
they and shift for thy selfe, for no helpe thou shalte

---

3 ¶ *omitted* C.          11 fyshe.] fyshe, C.          23 fyshe] syshe C.
25 myschiefe] mychiefe C.

haue of vs. And theare they lefte the Eele to bee
drowned.

### ¶ The viii. tale.

O N a time the men of Gotam had forgotten to
paye theyr rent to their Lord. The one sayd to
the other, to morow is our pay day, and what
reamedy shall we fynde to sende our money to oure
Lorde? The one sayde thys daye I haue taken a
quicke Hare, and he shall carye it, for he is lyght of
foote. Be it sayde all, he shal haue a letter, and a
purse to put in our money and wee wyll tell hym
the | waye. When the Letters weare wryt, and the   [A8
money put into a pursse, they dyd tye them aboute
the Hares necke sayinge, fyrste thou must go to
Lowghburrow, and then to Leyceter, and at new-
warke theare is our Lorde, and commende vs to
him, and theare is hys dutye. The hare as soone as
hee was out of theyr handes, he did run a clene con-
trary way: Some cryed out to hym sayinge thou
must goe to Lowghburrow fyrste. Some sayde lett
the Hare alone, he can tel a nearer way then the
best of vs all: let him go.

### ¶ The ix. tale.

O N a tyme theare was one of Gotam mowynge in
the meades, and found a great gras- | hopper.   [A8ᵛ
He dyd caste downe hys sythe and dyd runne home

10

20

30

---

4 ¶ *omitted* C.      27 ¶ *omitted* C.

to his neighbours and sayde that there was a
Deuill in the fyelde that hopped in the grasse.
Then there was euerye man readye wythe clubbes
and staues, wythe Holbardes, and other weapons,
to go to kill the Grashopper. Whan they did come
to the place where that the Grashopper shoulde bee.
Sayde the one to the other, lette euerye man crosse
hym selfe from this deuill, for we wyll not meddle
wyth hym. And so they returned home againe and
10 sayde, wee weare well bleste thys daye that we
went no further. A cowardes sayd he that had the
sythe in the mead, helpe me to fetch my sithe. No
saide they, it is good to sleape in a whole skynne:
better it is to | leese thy sithe, then to mar vs all.   [B1


### ¶ The x. tale.


20 ON a certaine tyme theare weare twelue of
Gotam did goe a fysshyng, and some did wade
in the water, and some stoode a drye lande. And
when that they went homewarde, the one sayde to
the other, wee haue ventured farre to day in wadyng
I pray god that none of vs (that dyd come from
home) bee drowned. Marye sayde the one to the
other, let vs see that, for theare dyd twelue of vs
come oute. And they tolde themselues, and euerre
man dyd tell a leuen, and the twelfe man dyd
30 neuer tell hym selfe. Alas sayde the one to the other
there is one of vs drowned. | They went backe to   [B1ᵛ
the brooke whear that they had ben fishing and

---

4 wythe] wythe, C.        6 to the] co rhe C.        16 ¶ *omitted* C.

sought vp and down for him that was drowned,
and dyd make great lamentacion. A Courtyer dyd
come ridyng by and dyd aske what that they dyd
seeke. And whye they weare so sorye. O sayd they
this daye we wente to fysshe this brooke and there
dyd come out twelue of vs, and one is drowned.
Why said the Courtier tell how many be of you.
And the one tolde .xi. and hee dyd not tell himselfe. Well sayd the Courtier what will you geue
mee and I wyll fynd out twelue men? Syr sayde
they, al the money that we haue. Geue mee the
money sayde the courtier. And he began with the
fyrste, and did geue him a recombentibus ouer
the shoulders that | he groned, and sayd there is [B2
one: so he serued all that they groned on the matter.
When he dyd come to the laste he payde him a good
sayinge, here is the twelfe man. Gods blessing on
your hart sayd all the companie, that you haue
found out our neighbour.

¶ The xi. tale.

THere was a man of Gotam did ride by the way
and did find a cheese in the hye way, and he puld
out his sword, and poryd and pricked with the
poynte of his swerd to take vp the cheese. Theare
did come another man by and did a lyght and toke
vp the chese and rid his way. The man of gotam did
ride back to Nottingham to buye a longer swerd to
take vp the cheese. And when he had bought his

---

15-16 matter. When] matter when C.     26 puld] puld, C.

swerd he returned back. | And when he did come    [B2ᵛ]
to the place wheare the cheese dyd lye he pulled out
his swerde and prycked at the grounde sayinge, a
murryon take it, if I had had thys swerde I had had
the cheese.

¶ The .xii. tale.

10

THere was a man of Gotam and hee dyd not loue
his wyfe: and she hauinge a fayre heare, hir
husbande said diuers times that he would cut it of,
and he durste not doe it when she was waking, but
when she was a sleape. So on a night he toke vp a
paire of sheres and layde them vnder hys beads
head, the whyche the wyfe perceyued. And then
shee dyd call to her one of her maydes and sayde, go
to bead to my husband, for hee | is mynded to cut    [B3
20 of my heare to nyght, let hym cut of thy heare, and
I wyll giue thee as good a kyrtle as euer thou dydst
weare. The mayde dyd so, and faynded her selfe a
sleape the whiche the man perceyuyng cut of the
maydes heare and dyd wrap it about the sheres and
layde it vnder hys beaddes head, and fell a sleape.
The wyfe made her mayde to aryse, and tooke the
heare and the sheres, and went into the hall and
burnte the heare. This man had a horse the which
hee dyd loue aboue all thynges. The wyfe went into
30 the stable, and cut of the horse tayle, and dyd wrap
the sheres in the horse tayle, and layd it vnder hir
husbands heade. In the mornynge shee dyd ryse be

---

time, and did sit by the fire keyming hir head. At
last the man did come | to the fire, and seynge his    [B3ᵛ]
wife keyming hir hed marueiled on it. The maide
seing her master standyng in a browne studie saide,
what a deuil aileth the horse in the stable for he
bledeth sore, the good man ran into the stable, and
founde that his horse taile was cut of, hee went to
his beads head and did finde the sheres wrapt in hys
horse taile, and did com to his wife saying, I cry the
10   merci for I had thought that I had cut of thy heare
to night, and I haue cut of my horse tayle. Ye sayd
she, selfe do selfe haue, manye a man thinketh to do
another man a shrewde turne, and turnethe oft
tymes to his owne selfe.

## ¶ The .xiii. tale.

20   THere was a man in Gotam that layde a wager
wythe hys wyfe that shee shoulde | not make    [B4]
him cokold. No said she but I can. Spare not said
he, do what thou canste. On a tyme she hyd al the
spyggots and fassets in the house, and shee went
into her butterie and set a barrell a broche, and
cryed to her husband and sayde, I praye you brynge
me heather a spyggot and a fasset, or else al the ale
wyll runne out. The good man sought vp and downe
and coulde fynde none. Come hether sayde she than,
30   and holde your fynger in the tap hole. She pulled
out her finger, and the good man put in hys. She
then called to her a Tayler the whyche did dwell at

---

3 it. The] it the C.      7 of,] of C.      12 she,] she C.
23 canste.] canste, C.      24 spyggots] sypggots C.

the nexte doore, with whom shee made a blinde bargayne. And wythin a whyle shee did come to her
husbande. (and ded brynge a spiggot and a fasset
with hir saying | pul out your finger out of the tap          [B4ᵛ
hole gentle Cockold for you haue lost your bar-
gayn. I beshrew thy hart for thy labour said the
good man. Make no suche bargaynes then sayde
she with me.

10

¶ The xiiii. tale.


THeare was a man of Gotam that had take a
     Bustard, and to the eating of it hee did bid .iiii.
or .v. gentlemens seruaunts. The wyfe had kylled
an olde broode goose: and she and two of hir gos-
seps had eaten vpp the Bustarde. The olde goose was
layde to the fyre for the gentlemens seruants. Whan
20   that they were come, and the old goose set before
them, what is this sayd one of the men? The good-
man said, a good fat bustard. | A bustard said          [B5
they? it is an olde goose, and thou arte a knaue to
mocke vs. And in a great anger they departed out of
the house and went home. The fellow was sory that
the gentlemans seruauntes weare angry, and dyd
take a bag and dyd put in the Bustardes fethers, and
thought to go to them and shew them the fethers
of the Bustarde, and so to please them. The wife
30   prayed hir husband (or he wente) to fetche in a
blocke to the fyre: and in the meane space she dyd
put out all the Bustardes fethers, and dyd put in the

---

2 bargayne.] bargyne. C.          20 they] tbey C.
22 *The* a *of* bustard *inverted* C.          26 the] tke C.

goose fethers. The man takynge hys poake or bag,
went to the gentlemens seruauntes and sayde, I
pray you be not angrye wyth mee for you shall see
here that I had a bustard, for here be the fethers: and
| he opened his bag, and did shake out the goose    [B5ᵛ
fethers. The gentlemens seruants seing the goose
fethers sayde, why knaue couldest thou not be con-
tented to mocke vs at home at thine owne house,
but art come to mock vs here, the one tooke a
waster, and dyd geue hym a dosen stripes sayng,
take this for a reward, and mock vs no more.

### ¶ The xv. tale.

THeare was a yonge man of Gotam the which
should go a woing to a faire maid: his mother
did warne hym sayinge, when thou dost loke vpon
her, cast a sheepes eye and saye, how do ye sweete
pygges nye? The fellowe went to the butchers and
bought .vii. or .viii. sheepes eyes, and when thys
lusty woer did sit at diner he wold | loke vpon his    [B6
faire wench and wold caste in hir face a sheepes eye
sayinge, how do you my pigges nye. how do I
said the wench, swines face, why doest thou cast
the sheepes eye vpon me. O sweete piggs eye sayd
he, haue at thee another. I defye thee swynes face
sayde the wenche. The fellow beinge abasshed sayd,
what sweete pygge be content, for and if thou do
liue vntill the next yeare, thou wilt be a foule sow.
Walk knaue walk sayd she, for if thou dost liue tel

---

6 fethers.] fethers, C.
26 said the wench,] (said the wēch C.

the nexte yeare, thou wilt be a starke knaue, a lub-
ber, and a foole. Here a man may see, for a mans
good will, he shall haue euill will and displeasure.

## ¶ The xvi. tale.

A Mans wife of Gotam was brought a bed of a
man child. | The father dyd byd the gossops, [B6ᵛ]
the whiche were chyldren of viii. or nyne yeares of
age. The eldest childes name that should be god-
father was named Gylbert. The second chyld was
named Humfry. And the godmothers name was
Christabell. The friends of them dyd monyshe them
sayinge, that dyuers tymes they must say after the
prieste. Whan all weare come to the church dore,
the priest said, be you agreed of the name? be you
said Gylbert agreed of the name? Be you sayde
Humfry agreed of the name. Be you said Chrysta-
bell agreed of the name, the priest sayd whearfore
bee you come hether? Gylbert sayde, wherefore be
you come hether. Humfry said wherefore bee you
come hether Christabell sayde whearfore, be you
come | hether. The priest being amased coulde not [B7]
tell what to saye, but whisteled and saide whew,
Gylbert whisteled and said whew, Humfry whistled
and said whew, and so did Christabell. The priest
being angry said, go home fooles go home Go home
fooles go home said gilbert, go home fooles go hom
said Humfry, go home fooles go home said Christa-

---

1 t *of* wilt *not printed* C.  3 displeasure.] dipleasure. C.
10 child.] child C.  20 Humfry] Hūiry C.

bell. The priest then prouided for Godfathers and Godmothers. Here a man maye see that chyldren can do nothing with out good instructions. And they be not wise that wil regard childrens wordes.

## ❡ The xvii. tale.

THere was a man of Gotam the whych shuld be maried, and when the day of maryage was | appoynted, and the time came that they shoulde [B7ᵛ] be maried together, the priest sayd say after me. The man said say after me. The priest said, say not after me such words but say after me as I wil tel thee. The fellow said, say not after me such wordes, but saye after me as I will tell thee. The priest sayde, thou dost playe the foole and the knaue, to mock with this holy sacrament of matrymony. The fellow said, thou dost play the foole and the knaue to mock with this holie sacrament of matrymonye. The priest could not tell what to say, but said what shal I do with this foole? The felow said, what shal I doe with this foole. Farewell sayde the prieste, I wyll not marrie thee. Farewell sayde the fellow, I wyll not marrye thee. | The prieste departed: how [B8] bee it the fellow (by other men) was instructed how to doe: and after that hee was maryed. And I hard say such a folish pranke was played at Kingston of late dayes.

## ¶ The xviii. tale.

THeare was a Scottish man the whiche dyd dwell
at gotam, and hee had taken an house a lytle
from London, and of it he would make an Inne, and
to his Signe hee woulde haue a Bores head. And he
wente to London to haue a Bores head made. He
dyd come to a Caruer (or a Joyner) saying in his
mother tonge, I saye spek, kens thou meke me a
Bare heade? Ye said the Caruer. | Than sayd the
skotyshman, mek me a bare head anenst Yowle, an
thowse bus haue xx pence for thy hyre. I wyll doe
it sayde the Caruer. On S. Andrewes daye before
Chrystmas (the which is named Yowle in Scotland,
and in England in the north) the skottish man did
com to London for his Bores heade to set at a dore
for a signe. I say speke said the skotish man, haste
thou made me a Bare head? Yea said the Caruer.
Then thowse a gewd fellow. The Caruer went and
did bryng a mans head of wod that was bare and
sayd, syr here is youre bare head. I say sayde the
skotyshman, the mokyl deuill, is this a bare head?
Ye said the caruer. I say sayd the Skotishman, I will
haue a bare head, syk an head as doth follow | a
Sew that hath Gryces. Syr said the caruer, I can not
tel what is a Sew, nor what is a Gryce. Whet
herson, kenst thou not a sew that wil greet and
grone, and her gryces wil run after her and cry a
weke a weke. O said the Caruer, it is a pigge. Yea
said the skotish man, let me haue his fathers head

[B8ᵛ

[C1

---

2 ¶ *omitted* C.    12 heade?] heare? C.
17 north)] north.) C.    23 *The* a *of* sayde *inverted* C.
28 Whet] whet C.

made in timber, and mek me a bird and set it on his
skalps, and cause her to sing whip whir, whip
whir. The caruer sayde, I can not cause her to singe
whip whir. Whe horson sayde the skotish man gar
her as she woulde singe whip whir.
Here a man maye see that euerye man doth delight in his owne sences, or doth reioice in his
fantasie.

10                 ¶ The xix. tale.

IN old time when as these afore said Iestes was (as
men of that | cuntrey reporteth) that such fan-    [C1ᵛ
tasticall matters weare done at gotam (the which I
can not tell halfe.) The wyues weare gathered
together in an alehouse. And the one sayde to the
other that they weare all profitable to their husbandes. Whyche waye good gossips sayd the Ale-
20  wife. The fyrste sayd, I shall tell you all good gossips: I can neither bake nor brew nor I can doe no
worke, whearefore I do make euery day holiday
and I go to the alehouse, bicause at all times I
cannot go to the church, and in the alehouse I
praye to God to speede well my husband. And I do
think my praier shal do him much more good then
my labour if I could worke. Then sayde the second,
I am profitable to my husband in sauing of candels
in winter | for I do cause my husband and al my    [C2
30  house folkes to go to bead by daylighte, and to rise
by daylight. The thyrd wife sayd, and I am profyt-
able to my husbande in spending of bread, for I will

---

8 fantasie.] fantasie C.
17 *space after* alehouse *but period not printed* C.

eate but litle, for to the drinckyng of a galon or two
of good ale, I care for no meate. The fourth wife
saide, I am loth to spend meat and drinke at
home in my owne house, wherfore I do go to the
wine tauerne at Nottingham, and do take wine,
and such things as god shal send me theare. The
fifte wyfe sayd a man shall euer haue more compa-
nye in another mans house then his owne, (and
most commonlye in an Alehouse is the best cheare
in a towne.) And for sparing of meate and drynke
and other necessaryes, I do go to the alehouse. The
sixt | wife said, my husband hath woll, and flax      [C2ᵛ]
and tow: and to spare it, I go to other mens houses
to do other mens worke. The seuenth wife said, I do
spare my husbands wood and cole, and do sit talk-
ing al the day by other mens fires. The eight said,
beefe, mutton, and porcke is dere, wherfore I doe
spare it, and do take pigge, goose, hen, chicken
conye and capon, the which be of lower pryce. The
ninth said, and I do spare my husbands sope and lye,
for when hee shoulde be wasshed once in a weeke,
I doe wash once in a quarter of a yeer. Then sayd
the alewife, and I doe keepe my husbandes ale (that
I do brew,) from sowryng. For wheare as I was
wont to drynke vp all, nowe I do leaue neuer a
drop. |

### ¶ The .xx. tale.                                   [C3]

ON Ashwednesday the priest of gotam wold make
a colacion to his parishoners and said, freyndes

---

28 ¶ omitted C.

the tyme is come that you must vse praier and
fasting, and almes dedes, and this weke cum you to
shryfte, and I wyll tel you more of my mynd, for as
for prayers, I thinke theare bee not two persons in
the parish can say halfe their Pater noster. As for
fasting, you fast styll: for you haue not a good
meales meat through the whole yeare. As for almes
dedes, what shuld you do to giue any thyng, that
hath nothing to take to. But when that you doe
come to shrift, I will tel you more of my mynd.
After masse, the good man that did keepe the alehouse, did come to shrift, and aboue al thinges hee
confessed hymselfe to bee | drunck diuers times in      [C3ᵛ]
the yeere, specially in Lent. The priest sayd in Lent
thou shouldest moste refraine from drunkenes, and
abstaine from drinke. Not so said the fellow, for it
is an old prouerbe that fishe must swim. Ye sayd the
prieste, it must swim in water. I crye God mercy
sayd the fellow, I thought it shuld haue swom in
good ale.

### ¶ The xxi. tale.

SO one after another the men of Gotam did come
to shrift, and whan they were shryuen the
priest said I cannot tell what penaunce to geue you.
If I should enioyne you to prayer, there is non of you
that can say your Pater noster, and you be now
to old to learne. And to enioyne you to fast, it
weare but folyshnes, for you doe not eate a good

---

31 enioyne] enioye C.

meales meate in a yeare.  | Wherfore I do inioyne   [C4
the to labour wel the weeke, that thou maist
fare wel to diner on the sondaies: and I wil
come to dinner and see that it be so, and take
part. Another man hee dyd enioyne to fare well
the monday. And another the tuesday. And so
one after another, that one or other shoulde
fare well once a weeke, that hee myght haue
parte of the meate. And as for almes deedes
the priest sayd, you be but beggers
all, excepte it be one or two,
therfore bestowe the almes
on youre owne selues.

10

## FINIS.

20

Imprinted at London in Fletstret, be-
neath the Conduit, at the signe of
S. Iohn Euangelist, by
Thomas Colwell.

---

3 fare wel] farewel C.          4 dinner] dnner C.
23 the Conduit,] thf Conduit, C.

R. I.,

# The History of Tom Thumbe

*Edited by Curt F. Bühler*

# Introduction

*It is needless to mention the popularity of the following story. Every city, town, village, shop, stall, man, woman, and child, in the kingdom, can bear witness to it. Its antiquity, however, remains to be enquired into, more especially as no very ancient edition of it has been discovered.*

One hundred and seventy years ago, Joseph Ritson [1] set down this observation in his reprint of the metrical version of the life of Tom Thumb, the edition printed in London for John Wright, 1630. [2] It is quite as true today, as our knowledge of the early printing history of this legend has advanced not one jot beyond the information

---

1. *Pieces of Ancient Popular Poetry: from Authentic Manuscripts and Old Printed Copies* (London, 1791), p. [94]. The 1630 metrical version was also reprinted by W. C. Hazlitt in *Remains of the Early Popular Poetry of England* (London 1864–66), II, 175–192.

2. STC 24115.

available to a scholar in the closing years of the eighteenth century.

By a curious coincidence, Ritson was then the possessor of the sole surviving copy of the original 1621 edition which is the concern of the present reprint.[3] Commenting on this edition, Ritson remarked: "This however was only the common metrical story turned into prose with some foolish additions by R. I. [Richard Johnson]." Despite this assertion, a comparison of the extant metrical and prose versions indicates that the 1630 metrical version, in its earlier part at least, is merely a metaphrase of the 1621 prose version. Ritson reprinted part of the "Introductory Chapter" in his own foreword; though the *Dictionary of National Biography*[4] speaks of Ritson's "passion for minute accuracy" and his "impatience of inaccuracy," he managed to misspell four words and altogether omit two others.

Nor was this the only portion of the prose Tom Thumb which could be consulted by a serious student prior to the present reprint, the first (so far as can be discovered) of the work *in toto*. In the commentary attached to his edition of Shakespeare's *As You Like It* (III. ii. 220: "You must borrow me Gargantua's mouth first"),[5] the scholarly but devious James Orchard Halliwell[-Phillipps] reprinted the entire account of Tom Thumb's encounter with Gargantua. This reprint is as scrupulously correct

---

3. For a description of this chapbook, see Frederick B. Adams, Jr., *Fifth Annual Report to the Fellows of the Pierpont Morgan Library* (New York, 1954), pp. 38–40.

4. XLVIII, 328 and 330.

5. *The Works of William Shakespeare* (London, 1853–1865), VI, 191–192.

as the editor's character was not.[6] But it is as certain as such things can be that the surviving editions of neither the prose nor the metrical versions were the actual first printings of the several forms of the legend. Both volumes are decorated with woodcuts illustrating events in the life of that great little man, Tom Thumb, and in both editions the blocks show such signs of wear as could only come from earlier use—and, apparently, from repeated earlier use. If such presumed editions were actually produced, no vestige of them has descended to our day.

References to the legend appear in English literary accounts more than a third of a century before the first (extant) printing of Tom Thumb. In William Fulke's *D. Heskins . . . ouerthrowne* (London: H. Middleton for G. Bishop, 1579, p. 235) there is the statement, "They feigned him to be a little child like Tom Thumb." And Reginald Scot, in *The Discouerie of Witchcraft* (London: W. Brome, 1584, pp. 152–153),[7] reports: "But in our childhood our mothers maids haue so terrified vs with . . . the fierdrake, the puckle, Tom thombe, hob gobblin, Tom tumbler, boneles, and such other bugs, that we are afraid of our owne shadowes."

It has been said [8] that our hero—possibly also his Ger-

---

6. See A. N. L. Munby, *The Family Affairs of Sir Thomas Phillipps* (Phillipps Studies no. 2) (Cambridge, 1952), and D. A. Winstanley, "Halliwell Phillipps and Trinity College Library," *The Library*, Fifth ser., II (1948), 250–282.

7. STC 21864, copy at the Folger Shakespeare Library. For a transcript of these lines, I am much obliged to Dr. James G. McManaway.

8. Dr. Harry B. Weiss, "Three Hundred Years of Tom Thumb," *The Scientific Monthly*, XXXIV (1932), 157–166.

man and Scandinavian counterparts (Däumling, Tom-meliden, and the rest)—is no more than a survivor of a quaint "swallow cycle," so named for the obvious reasons to be discovered in the text, which apparently formed part of the very ancient and universal stock of Indo-European folk tales. To modern tastes, indeed, some of the episodes recounted here are quite repugnant, and Harry B. Weiss has wisely remarked that "under no circumstances is Tom now allowed to get beyond the cow's mouth." Scatological humor, on the other hand, appealed to the seventeenth century!

Having made his appearance in English literature, Tom Thumb quickly entrenched his position as a literary figure, and his "small bignesse" can be encountered at least twice more before the publication of his *Life*, as here reissued. In 1592 Thomas Nashe referred to him, though in no friendly manner, in his *Pierce Penilesse*,[9] while in 1611 James Field cited him casually in some verses prefixed to Thomas Coryate's *Crudities*.[10] Three years after the publication of the prose version, in 1624, our Tom was given a very minor role in Ben Jonson's masque, *The Fortunate Isles*,[11] and in 1627 "Tom Thum a Fayrie Page" appeared a number of times in

9. STC 18371, B2; copy in the Arents Collection, New York Public Library. Ronald B. McKerrow (*The Works of Thomas Nashe*, Oxford, 1910, IV, 90) observes: "I cannot learn of any book on Tom Thumb of so early a date."

10. STC 5808, l1; copy in The Pierpont Morgan Library. James Field is listed by Franklin B. Williams, Jr., *Index of Dedications and Commendatory Verses in English Books before 1641* (London, 1962), p. 67.

11. STC 14772, C1-C1ᵛ; copy in the Carl H. Pforzheimer Library, New York.

Michael Drayton's *Nimphidia*.[12] By the time the metrical version had made its appearance in 1630, "the peculiar greatness of his littleness" (as Hazlitt termed it) [13] had already firmly impressed itself as a permanent fixture in the stream of England's literary tradition, not only as a subject dear to the hearts of countless generations of children but also as a source of entertainment for the adult world. The instances just cited confirm the view that, though the prose Tom Thumb is the earliest which has yet been discovered, accounts of his life must have been circulating widely throughout England for many decades prior to the first publication of this tract.

Ritson, Halliwell,[14] the *Dictionary of National Biography*,[15] and the *Cambridge Bibliography of English Literature* [16] unhesitatingly ascribe the prose Tom Thumb to the pen of Richard Johnson (1573–1659?), partly on the strength of the initials found at the end of the work and partly because the nature of the present tract is entirely in keeping with the author's known literary output. Such works as *The Most Famous History of the Seauen Champions of Christendome*,[17] *Look on me London, The Pleas-*

---

12. In Drayton's *The Battaile of Agincourt*, STC 7190, Q2ᵛ etc.; copy in the Morgan Library.

13. William Carew Hazlitt, "Tom Thumb," *The Connoisseur*, VII (1903), 234–237.

14. *The Metrical History of Tom Thumb the Little, as issued early in the Eighteenth Century* (London, 1860), p. 7.

15. Under entry for Richard Johnson, XXX, 25.

16. (Cambridge, 1940–57), I, 730.

17. (London, 1596), STC 14677. Copy seen: London [1626], STC 14682, Pforzheimer Library.

*ant Walkes of Moore-Fields*,[18] *The Pleasant Conceites of Old Hobson*,[19] and *The Most Pleasant History of Tom a Lincolne* [20] have an obvious kinship to the fable here reprinted. Perhaps it is not without significance that "Tom Lincolne" is specifically mentioned in the first chapter—and this may suggest that some of the other titles cited there were written (or, possibly, rewritten) by Richard Johnson.[21] Since the earliest edition of his *Tom a Lincolne* known to the *Short-Title Catalogue* is "the sixth impression," the mortality rate for such printings was manifestly stupendous, and the lack of concrete proof, in the form of surviving editions, does not render this supposition untenable. The *Dictionary of National Biography* [22] also recalls "the frequent incorporation of blank verse of no mean quality in Johnson's prose narrative, and his numerous adumbrations, sometimes amounting to direct quotations, of Shakespeare." Metri-

---

18. Both works printed in John Payne Collier, *Illustrations of Early English Popular Literature* (London, 1863–64), II. The first contains a dedication to Sir Thomas Middleton, Lord Mayor of London, signed "R. I." STC 14676 and 14690.

19. (London, 1607), STC 14688. Reprinted in the W. C. Hazlitt series, "Old English Jest-Books" (London, 1866).

20. (London, 1631), STC 14684. In the seventh impression ([London, 1635], STC 14685, copy New York Public Library), the Preface is also signed "R. I."

21. Ritson (*Pieces of Ancient Popular Poetry*, pp. 1–30) prints a metrical *Adam Bel, Clym of the Cloughe, and Wyllyam of Cloudesle* (STC 1807), of which he says [p. 2]: "there is no other memorial of these celebrated archers than the following legend." Possibly Johnson rewrote (or planned to rewrite) this piece into a prose version.

22. XXX, 24.

cal passages are, of course, found in the prose Tom Thumb, and pale (very pale indeed) adumbrations of Shakespearean motifs will be seen in the character of Gargantua (to which reference has already been made), the stanza with "Fi, fee, fau, fan" (*King Lear*, III. iv. 175),[23] and the account of the headless creatures (*Othello*, I. iii. 167–168, and *The Tempest*, III. iii. 64). If the Shakespearean allusions suggested these topics to Richard Johnson, then he must surely have sought elsewhere for further and more detailed information.

But where did he seek? Nowadays "Fee, Fi, Fo, Fum" is to be found in *Jack and the Bean-Stalk* and in *Jack the Giant-Killer*, though neither Jack [24] was immortalized in print till long after Tom Thumb had achieved this distinction. Then too, Tom and the giant-killing Jack also shared the magic seven-leagued shoes and the power of invisibility—Tom by means of a ring and Jack through a cloak. Since time immemorial, adults as well as children have been enthralled by mysterious powers and magical qualities, from the invulnerability of Siegfried and the linden leaf that shattered it (as Thetis had shattered that of Achilles!), through the mushroom that did such strange things to the person of Alice, to the incredible faculties of Superman. The Fairy Queen, her

---

23. Compare Halliwell's edition and his notes (*Works*, XIV, 465) and McKerrow (*Thomas Nashe*, IV, 320) for earlier uses of this line.

24. Concerning Jack and the Giants, Halliwell (as in previous note) states: "The earliest known edition of this story bears the date of 1711, a mistake, I believe from the character of the type, for 1771 or, possibly, 1741, but it is certainly not so old as the date given, 1711." The earliest printing of *Jack and the Bean-Stalk* cited in the 1881–1900 British Museum catalogue is [1810?].

attendants, and the clothes and gifts which she bestowed on Tom belong to this ancient and shadowy world of enchantment. All these and the now-famous man-threatening stanza quite evidently formed part of the common store of British folklore, and doubtless it was there that Richard Johnson found them. And where there are giants and dwarfs, there must needs be pygmies; so one recalls that, according to the *OED*, "twattle" has served as a generic name for a small human being ever since 1598. In the present version, however, King Twaddell (or Twadle—consistency of spelling was not a virtue of either Johnson or the printer) plays a very insignificant role.

The impressive form of Gargantua made its first appearance in English literature in 1547.[25] It is almost certain that, before the turn of the century, editions of his "prophecy" and his "history" had already been published.[26] However, since no copies of such printings have survived, it cannot be determined whether Richard Johnson drew upon these or on the original French text. Two printed versions of the latter have come down to us,

---

25. *The Boke of Marchauntes* (London: R. Jugge, 1547) STC 3322; cf. F. P. Wilson, "The English Jestbooks of the Sixteenth and Early Seventeenth Centuries," *The Huntington Library Quarterly*, II (1939), 134.

26. The following entries are found in the Registers of the Company of Stationers: "6 April 1592. John Wolf. Entred vnto him for his Copie vnder the hande of master Hartwell Gargantua his prophesie . . . vj^d" (Arber, II, 607); "16 June 1592. [Entry canceled] Entred for his Copie vnder the hand of master Abraham Hartwell A booke entytuled, Gargantua . . . [no sum stated]" (Arber, II, 613); and "4 Dec. 1594. John Danter. Entred for his Copie vnder the handes of the wardens. A booke entituled the historie of Gargantua. &c. Provided that if this Copie doo belonge to anie other, Then this Entrance to be voide . . . vj^d" (Arber, II, 667).

familiarly known as the *Grandes Croniques* of 1532 and the *Croniques Admirables* of two years later.[27] One of these—or perhaps even a third text—was translated into English before 1572, and the *Croniques Admirables* must have been available in such a translation a score of years later.[28] Gargantua's horse "of that great bignesse, as is described in the booke of his honourable deedes" is certainly "la grant iument" of both chronicles,[29] but at least one of the giant's boasts to Tom Thumb is paralleled by Rabelais' own narrative—for there Gargantua is guilty of drowning 260,418, not counting women and small children.[30] The spelling of the name *Garagantua* also calls for comment. Reliable sources [31] recall to mind that this misspelling (if such it be) began in Shake-

---

27. *Les grandes et inestimables Croniques du grant et enorme geant Gargantua*, Lyon, 1532, and *Les Croniques admirables du puissant Roy Gargantua* [1534]; cf. Graesse, *Trésor*, VI, 2–3. Both texts were reprinted by Huntington Brown in his edition of François Girault, *The Tale of Gargantua and King Arthur* (Cambridge, Mass., 1932).

28. Cf. Huntington Brown, *Rabelais in English Literature* (Cambridge, Mass., 1933), p. 32.

29. The delicacy of Tom Thumb's diet and clothing stands in sharp contrast to the grossness of Gargantua's consumption of food and the size of his wardrobe.

30. "Il en noya deux cens soixante mille, quatre cens dixhuict, sans les femmes & petits enfans" (*Les Oeuvres de M. Francois Rabelais, Docteur en Medecine* [A Lyon, Par Pierre Estiard, 1580], p. 65; copy in New York Public Library).

31. For example, Horace Howard Furness ("As You Like It," *A New Variorum Edition of Shakespeare* [Philadelphia, 1890], p. 161), Clarence L. Barnhart (*The New Century Handbook of English Literature* [New York, 1956], p. 474), etc.

speare's works with the edition sponsored by Alexander Pope, but the variant spelling is here shown to be both very old and very respectable so far as English literature is concerned.

Lastly the men without heads, those with but one eye and that in their foreheads, and the other monstrous figures seen by Tom Thumb on his flight to another world found their way into this prose text from the English versions of Mandeville, Pliny, or Ptolemy, either directly or indirectly through any of the many works which drew upon these boundless stocks of the fabulous.[32] These, then, are some of the "foolish additions" supplied by Richard Johnson.

A distinct odor of the unfinished and incomplete pervades the prose Tom Thumb.[33] In his preface, the author proclaims that he will relate no tales "of Garragantua that monster of men"—only, as already noted, to devote a considerable section to this disagreeable figure toward the close of his narrative. Then tiny Tom, as a turnspit for the giant in the castle, is assigned an utterly

---

32. Compare Josephine Waters Bennett, *The Rediscovery of Sir John Mandeville* (New York, 1954), especially Chapter 16. It is interesting, too, to recall that the hanging of pots and glasses on a sunbeam by Tom Thumb appears to be the survival of a very ancient tradition. Ludwig Bieler (*Ireland: Harbinger of the Middle Ages* [London, 1963], p. 110) remarks: "One particular type of miracle, however, namely that in which a saint hangs his or her wet garment on a sunbeam to dry, has plausibly been derived from a story in the Legend of St. Brigit."

33. At the very beginning of the new chapter on signature A8ᵛ, a subject [Tom] is wanting for the verb "durst." Again, on B2, the same subject is presumably required for "drove" in order to complete the sense, while the following "hee" apparently does not refer to Old Thomas (as the previous ones had done). This passage is particularly awkward and unpolished.

anomalous role. Surely no piece of meat fit for so Cyclopean a man could possibly have been handled by our small hero. The last chapter heading promises an account of how Tom Thumb fared with King Twadle. All we are given, however, is Tom's bald statement to King Arthur that "this stout King did he ouerthrow at Tilt both horse and man." At the very end of the booklet, it is suggested that, "if it like the Reader," a continuation will be provided by the author. The assignment,[34] on 13 December 1620, of *"The first and 2. parte of Tom Thombe"* (Arber, IV, 44) indicates that this continuation at one time existed; but no copy is known.

This short preface, it is hoped, will throw some explanatory light on the legend of Tom Thumb as it is related in the prose text of 1621. When Dr. Samuel Johnson [35] thundered that, to avoid being subjected to a discourse on Catiline's conspiracy, "I withdrew my attention, and thought about Tom Thumb," the Great Cham of English literature conferred the ultimate accolade upon little Tom. In conclusion, it seems proper to recall that in 1711 William Wagstaffe [36] published a study of the legend, designed as a parody of classical scholarship

---

34. Assigned to Thomas Langley "by John Trundle and by Consent of Master Lownes warden." On 30 June 1623, Langley conveyed this to Lawrence Hayes (Arber, IV, 143), who in turn assigned it on 15 November 1628 to Francis Coules (Arber, IV, 204).

35. Percival Merritt, *The True Story of the so-called Love Letters of Mrs. Piozzi* (Cambridge, 1927), p. 70.

36. *A Comment upon the History of Tom Thumb* (London: Printed for J. Morphew, 1711), pp. 4–5. See also William K. Wimsatt, Jr., *Parodies of Ballad Criticism (1711–1787)* [The Augustan Reprint Society, Publication no. 63] (Los Angeles, 1957).

as practiced by the eminent Richard Bentley. But it may
be its own and just reward that the intended irony of his
comments actually came very close to approximating the
true, popular appeal which the story of Tom Thumb has
held for many people:

> The Design was undoubtedly to recommend Virtue,
> and to shew that however any one may labour under
> the Disadvantages of Stature or Deformity, or the
> Meanness of Parentage, yet if his Mind and Actions
> are above the ordinary Level, those very Disadvan-
> tages, that seem to depress him, shall add a Lustre
> to his Character.

## Description

The History of *Tom Thumbe*, the | *Little*, for his
small stature surnamed, | *King* ARTHVRS *Dwarfe:* |
Whose Life and aduentures containe many | strange
and wonderfull accidents, published for | *the delight
of merry Time-spenders.* | [woodcut] | Imprinted at
London for *Tho: Langley*. 1621.

The volume is an octavo, and the signatures run A-B⁸C⁴;
A1ᵛ is blank, and C4 is wanting (probably blank). The
woodcut on the title page, depicting the incidents of
Tom Thumb and the pudding-bowl, his being eaten by
the cow and carried aloft by the raven, seems to be much
worn, indicating that it had been used previously for
other editions of the adventures of Tom Thumb. The
running title, omitted on A2, is "The History | of *Tom*

*Thumbe."* (*"Thumbe"* is spelled *"Thumb"* on A3 and C3, "of" is omitted on A7 and A8). There are no errors in catchwords, but B3ᵛ has no catchword and there is a spelling variation on A4ᵛ: shaddowes,/shadowes,.

The Pierpont Morgan Library copy (PML 45444), the only one known, is 5½ x 3½ inches, bound in nineteenth-century olive morocco. Its provenance is: Narcissus Luttrell (d. 1732); Edward Wynne (sale, 6 March 1786, lot 23); John Baynes (d. 1787); bequeathed to Joseph Ritson (sold 1803); Richard Heber (17 December 1834, lot 1743); Edward Vernon Utterson (April 1852, lot 1504; bought, according to Seymour de Ricci, *A Catalogue of Early English Books in the Library of John L. Clawson* [New York, 1924], p. 152, by James Orchard Halliwell); George Daniel (July 1864, lot 1684); Henry, then Alfred Huth (9 July 1919, lot 7474); John L. Clawson (May 1926, lot 425); Dr. A. S. W. Rosenbach (private collection); Robert H. Taylor, Esq.; presented by him to the Pierpont Morgan Library in February 1954. The copy contains the Utterson, Huth, and Clawson bookplates. References: STC 14056; Lowndes V, 2681; Clawson Catalogue (1924), no. 425; Frederick B. Adams, Jr., *Fifth Annual Report to the Fellows of the Pierpont Morgan Library* (New York, 1954), pp. 38–40 (with cut).

In the following reprint, abbreviations (& and macron over vowel) have been expanded silently, and "long s" has been printed "s". In the transcript of the title page (p. xvi), the running titles, and the chapter headings, the roman, italic, and roman small caps of the original have been kept; but in the body of the text the original black letter is printed in roman, the original roman in italic, and the original italic in roman small caps.

Title page of Langley's edition, 1621
*Courtesy of the Pierpont Morgan Library*

# The History of *Tom Thumbe*, the *Little*, for his small stature surnamed, *King* ARTHVRS *Dwarfe*:

Whose Life and aduentures containe many strange and wonderfull accidents, published for *the delight of merry Time-spenders.*

Imprinted at London for *Tho: Langley.* 1621.

The ornaments approximate the originals; the block
initial is facsimile, from the Pierpont Morgan Library.

# THE
# HISTORY OF
## TOM THVMBE, the Little,
### for his small stature, surna-
### med King ARTHVRS
### *Dwarfe.*

Y merry Muse begets no Tales of *Guy* of *Warwicke*, nor of bould Sir *Beuis* of *Hampton;* nor will I trouble my Penne with the pleasant glee of *Robin Hood*, little *Iobn*, the Fryer and his Marian; nor will I call to minde the lusty Pindar of *Wakefield*, nor those bold Yeomen of the North, *Adam Bell*, *Clem* of the *Clough*, nor *William* of *Cloudesly*, those an-
10 cient Archers of all England, nor shal my Story be made of the mad merry | pranckes of Tom of Bethlem, Tom Lincolne, or Tom a Lin, the Diuels supposed Bastard, nor yet of *Garragantua*

that monster of men, but of an older *Tom*, a *Tom* of
more antiquity, a *Tom* of a strange making, I meane
Little *Tom* of *Wales*, no bigger then a Millers
Thumbe, and therefore for his small stature, sur-
named *Tom Thumbe:* This is the Subiect that my Pen
meanes to make you merry with, and the onely
Story that (at noone dayes) may in time become the
awaker of sleepy Youth, prone to sluggishnesse:
The ancient Tales of *Tom Thumbe* in the olde time,
10   haue beene the onely reuiuers of drowzy age at mid-
night; old and young haue with his Tales chim'd
Mattens till the Cocks crow in the morning; Batche-
lors and Maides with his Tales haue compassed the
Christmas fire-blocke, till the Curfew Bell rings
candle out; the old Shepheard and the young Plow
boy after their dayes labour, haue carold out a Tale
of *Tom Thumbe* to make them merry with: and who
but little *Tom*, hath made long nights seeme short,
and heauy toyles easie? Therefore (gentle Reader)
20   considering with my selfe, that old modest mirth is
| turnd naked out of doores, while nimble wit in    [A3
the great Hall sits vpon a soft cushion giuing dry
bobbes; for which cause I will, if I can, new cloath
him in his former liuery, and bring him againe into
the Chimney Corner, where now you must imagine
me to sit by a good fire, amongst a company of good
fellowes ouer a well spic'd Wassel-bowle of Christmas Ale, telling of these merry Tales which hereafter follow.

## Of the birth and Parentage of *Tom Thumbe*, with his description and bignesse.

*I*N the old time, when King *Arthur* ruled this Land, the World was in a better frame then it is now: for then old plainnesse and ciuill society were companions for all companies: then, an vngarded Plowman might come vncontroled to a Royal Princes presence, and in those dayes the Countrey Husbandman was of the Kings Counsell, and in his russet Coate gaue as sound iudgement, as doe now many of our embrodred vpstarts in their robes of Tissue: for as then (in | this Land) learning was geason, and [A3ᵛ] the chiefest discipline in the world was Martiall actiuitie.

    Amongst many others of the Kings Councell, that attended in Court, there was a plaine Plowman, as then, called old *Thomas* of the Mountaine, which was the Kings owne Husbandman; for, as then, Princes maintained Shepheards, Neat-heards, Ploughmen, and such like, to keepe their Cattel, and till their grounds, with like busines of houshold Husbandry. This *Thomas* of the Mountaine, being a man well growne in yeares, long marryed, hauing a wife (as he thought) sufficient to bring children; but not blessed with that wished happinesse, often complayned to her in this manner: saying, Oh Wife

---

3 *Thumbe,*] *Tumbe*, L.

(quoth he) happy were I, if blessed with one Child:
one Child though it were no bigger then my thumb,
would make me happy: a child, of the very bignes of
my thumb would bring me the greatest content in
the world: Therfore would I haue thee (my deare
wife) go to the Prophet *Merlin*, and of him learne
the cause of thy barrennesse, and our wants in hau-
ing children; he is a man, rather a diuell or spi- |
rit, cunning in all Arts and Professions, all sciences,    [A4
10 secrets and discoueries, a coniurer, an inchanter, a
charmer, hee consorts with Elues and Fayries, a
Commaunder of Goblins, and a worker of Night-
wonders: hee can shew the secrets of Nature, calcu-
late childrens Birthes, and no doubt, but discouer
the cause of thy barrennesse, and bee a meanes to
procreate vs children: Away, and of him procure
this good blessing of a child, be hee no bigger then
my very Thumbe.

These reasons, and perswasions of olde *Thomas*, so
20 encouraged and whetted on this longing woman his
wife, that vp she got the next morning betime, and
by the Sunnes rise, came to the Caue of old *Merlin*,
which was the hollow trunke of a blasted Oke, all
ouer growne with withered mosse, (for other house
had hee none) whom shee found, as it were mum-
bling spels of incantation, making Characters in
sand, with an Ebone staffe, to the great wonder of
this poore affrighted Woman; who to satisfie her
Husbands desire, deliuered the ful effect of her busi-
30 nesse and comming. To whom *Merlin* with a graue
and solid countenance said as followeth: |

*Ere thrice the Moone her brightnes change,*                    [A4ᵛ]
*A shapelesse child by wonder strange,*
*Shall come abortiue from thy wombe,*
*No bigger then thy Husbands Thumbe:*
*And as desire hath him begot,*
*He shall haue life, but substance not;*
*No blood, nor bones in him shall grow,*
*Not seene, but when he pleaseth so:*
*His shapelesse shadow shall be such,*
10    *You'l heare him speake, but not him touch:*
*And till the World to ending come,*
*There shall be Tales told of* TOM THUMBE.

This *Ænygma*, or mysticall Riddle, no sooner deliuered, but home goes the merry old Wench to her
husband, and tels of her good successe, and of the
Oracle thus reuealed, how that within three
moneths space *Merlin* had promised her a litle
sonne: against which time, the father not a little
20    glad thereof, prouided all things fitting for such a
purpose, so that no necessaries were wanting
against his wiues lying in: but such a Child-bed
lying in was neuer seene nor heard of; for thither
came the Queene of Fayres to bee her Midwife, with
her attendants the Elues and Dryades, with such
like midnight dancing | shadowes, who gaue most        [A5]
diligent assistance, at that painfull houre of this
womans deliuerie. The child thus borne by the help
of this midnights Midwife, the Queene of Fayres,
30    had at the first minute it tooke life, the full and
largest bignes that euer it grew to: which was (as

---

25 attendants] atdendants L.

his Father wished) the bignesse of his Thumbe; and
therefore named *Tom Thumbe*, who neuer seemed
older, nor yonger; bigger, nor smaller; stronger, nor
weaker: but as he was at the first houre of his birth,
so continued hee to the last minute of his life.

---

### Of *Tom Thumbs* apparell, and of the sports he vsed amongst other Children.

10    *T*OM *Thumbe*, being thus by miracle begot and
borne, in lesse then foure minutes grew to be a
little man against which time the Queene of Fayres,
his kind Midwife, and good Godmother, prouided
him a very artificiall sute of apparell. First, a Hat
made of an Oken Leafe, with one feather of a Titti-
mouse tayle sticking in the same for a plume: his
Band | and Shirt being both sowed together, was   [A5ᵛ
made of a Spiders Cobweb, only for lightnesse and
20 soft wearing for his body: his cloth for his Doublet
and Hose, the tenth part of a dramme of Thistle-
downe weaued together: his Stockings the outward
Rinde of a greene Apple: his Garters two little
hayres pulled from his Mothers eyebrowes: as for
his Shooes and Bootes, they were made of a mouses
skin, tan'd into Leather: the largenesse wherof was
sufficient to make him twelue payre of Bootes, and
as many shooes and Pantofles. Thus furnisht forth
like a proper young Gallant, hee aduentured foorth
30 (though with great danger of the windes blowing
him away) into the streets, amongst other children
to play for Pins, Points, Counters, and such like,

but seldome played hee bankerupt: for like an inuisible Knight, he would at his pleasure (vnseene)
diue into his play-fellows pockets: where (before)
hauing lost, would there againe renew his stock,
and now and then, when hee pleased, would he
creep into their least cherrybags, and Pin-boxes. But
on a time, it so hapned, that for these his nimble
flights of actiuitie, he was most grieuously punished
| and imprisoned: for one of his play-fellowes kept     [A6
him fast pind vp in his pinbox the whole time of
schooling, without either meate, drinke, ayre, or
light though indeed hee could haue fasted for euer
without foode or sustenance, a gift that his Godmother the Queene of Fayries had giuen him at the
houre of his birth: yet for all this, *Tom Thumbe*,
hauing a desperate little spirit, like to his small bignesse, purposed to quittance these his former iniu-
ries done by his craftie companions; for indeed many
of them had serued him so.

___

How by art *Tom Thumbe* hung black Pots
and Glasses on the beames of the Sunne,
as vpon a line or cord: and of the
successe.

*T*OM *Thumb*, remembring his former imprisonment in his companions pinboxes, and Cherrybags, beate so together his nimble braines, that he
deuised a pretty reuenge: It so fell out, as his play-
fellowes and acquaintance were playing together,
hee got some of his mothers blacke Pots and

___

7 a time,] atime, L.        11 without] withont L.

Glasses, and most artificially hangd them | [vpon    [A6ᵛ
a] Sunne-beame, that shone in at the Schoole-house
window, at a little creuice, that made it seeme like
a small straight line or cord, vpon which hee or-
derly, to the others imaginations, hung vp his Pots
and Glasses all on a row. Which pretty trick when
the rest saw, they likewise got of their mothers
Pots and glasses, and in proffering to doe the like,
they broke them all in pieces: for which doings,
10    they had not onely the mockage of *Tom*, but thereby
wonne to themselues euery one a sound breching:
and euer after that, to their more disgrace, there
was a Rime made amongst the Schoole-boyes, as
hereafter followeth.

> *If thou wilt from whipping,*
>      *keepe safely thy bum,*
> *Take heed of the pastimes,*
>      *here taught by* TOM THUMBE:
> 20    *Young Schollers are knauish*
>      *and apter to learne*
> *A tricke that's vnhappy,*
>      *then good to discerne.* |

           [A7

---

How *Tom Thumbe* fell into his Mothers pudding Bowle: and of the first originall
of those Puddings now called *Tom*
*Thumbs*.

30    *T*Om Thumbe for these aforesaid merry tricks, was
     denied the fellowship of his Schoole-fellowes
and companions, which made him with great griefe

---

1–2 [vpon a] *not inked in text, catchword* vpon L.

stay at home in his fathers house, and to be gou-
erned onely by his mothers direction. But it so fell
out, that about Christmas time, his father had
killed a Hogge, and his mother was to make Puddings. And hauing all things ready: as Bloud, Oate-
meale, Suet, Salt and Spice all mingled, and well
seasoned together in a greate Bowle of wood; vpon
the side whereof, *Tom* was to sit (in stead of a Can-
dlesticke) to hold the Candle, and giue her light,
which he did so mannerly, as if hee had bin brought
vp a Candle holder. But now marke the euent: ether
*Tom* fell asleepe, or else being a little too nimble, or
of too light a timberd body, that of a suddaine hee
tipt and fell into the Pudding batter, quite ouer
head and eares Candle and all, the which his mother
spy- | ing, made hast with all speed to recouer him,        [A7ᵛ
but there shee found the Candle but not her Sonne:
for whome after shee had searched a long time, and
not finding him, supposed him to be drowned: with
griefe she ouerpassed her losse in a short time, (I
might say a minutes space) especially considering
him to be a child (for his littlenesse,) more dis-
graceful, then comfortable. So falling againe to her
businesse, shee tooke vp her small Sonne, and in
stead of a piece of fat, put him at vnawares into one
of her Puddings, which was of the largest size: the
which, with many others, shee cast into a kettle
then boyling ouer the fire. But now *Tom* feeling the
scalding liquor, and being in the middle of this
Pudding, made such a rumbling and tumbling vp
and downe the Kettle, that all the rest flew ouer
into the fire, choosing rather to be roasted, then

---

6 Suet,] Suet L.          31 that all] thatall L.

sodden: Some without skins, some without fashion,
some brok in pieces, some halfe sod, some one way,
some another as if the Diuell and old *Merlin* had
beene amongst them.

   This accident, or rather hurlyburly, amongst
*Toms* mothers puddings, made her thinke that they
were either bewitcht | or fore-spoke by some vn-      [A8
lucky tongue. Wherevpon, at that very instant
time, comes to the doore, a sturdy beging Tinker,
10 and asked an almes for good Saint *Iohns* sake: which
the Old Woman heareing, (and perceuing the vn-
rulines of that pudding in the Kettle) runs to the
same, and gaue it to the Tinker: who being there-
with well pleased, into his budget he puts it, and
hyes him away as fast as his legs can beare him. But
farre had he not gone, but the Pudding beganne to
rumble and tumble in the Tinkers budget, as it had
done before in the Pudding Kettle: which so affrighted the poore Tinker, that in going ouer a stile,
20 hee farted for very feare. Marry gip, good man
Tinker, quoth *Tom Thumbe;* are you farting ripe
with a wannion? hereupon the tinker (as he
thought) hearing the Diuell at his backe, threw
downe budget, Pudding, tooles and all, and ran
away as fast as his legges could beare him, not once
looking backe, till hee was out of all the hearing of
*Tom Thumb*, or the sight of his budget.

   The Tinker being thus gone, and *Tom Thumbe*
freed from his greasie Leather imprisonment, hee
30 eate himselfe at liber- | tie from his blacke bond-     [A8ᵛ
age, and returned home againe to his mothers

---

2 one way,] oneway, L.          11 perceuing] perceuiug L.
27 budget.] bndget. L.

house: where afterwards he told what had hapned,
and how he was carryed away bound vp in the Puddings belly; which happy escape and aduenture not
a little reioyced his old Father, and Mother, betwixt whom, and amongst many others, there arose
a name and title, belonging to al puddings of the
like roundnesse and thicknesse, and to be called
*Tom Thumbes:* Which name to the honour of all
Puddings, continues to this day.

10

---

How his mothers Red Cow, at one bit ate
vp *Tom Thumbe*, as he sate vnder
a Thistle.

*T*Hese fearefull dangers before rehearsed, being
thus happily ouerpassed, durst not by his
mother of a long time bee suffered to depart out of
20   her presence, but either she lockt him in her Cup-
bord for feare of losing him, or else tyed him to a
Brickbat with a Packthrid, doubting the wind
should blow him away: or else kept him in her
pocket for his more securitie: | But yet for all this,      [B1
another mischance befell him. For on a time, as his
mother went a-milking, *Tom* had a great desire to
goe with her, and to see that kinde of womanly
housewifery: Whereupon, she tooke vp her Sonne
and put him into her empty Milke-payle, and so
30   bore him to the fielde: where being come, and the
day very cold, shee set him downe vnder a Thistle

---

25 on a] one a L.        26 a-milking,] a milking, L.

for a shelter to keepe him warme, and so goes
a-milking of her Kine: but before shee had dis-
patched halfe her businesse, there comes a Red
Cow, and at one bit eates vp this litle man, her
Sonne, Thistle and all: But whether it was for
cowardlinesse or valor to sit still, I knowe not,
but poore *Tom* was eaten vp at one mouthfull,
where without chewing he went as easily downe
into the Cowes belly, as if he had beene made of a
docke leafe. But now all this while his mother not
missing him, but still milked on till her payle
grew full, and then being ready to goe home, she
looked for her sonne *Thomas*, where she neither
found him nor the thistle where she left him.
Whereupon she went vp and downe calling for *Tom*,
but no *Tom* was heard of. At last with great earnest-
nes (being much affrighted with this losse,) | she  [B1ᵛ]
went crying amongst her Kine, Where art thou
*Tom?* Where art thou, *Tom?* Here, Mother (quoth
he) in the Red Cowes belly: in the Red Cowes belly,
mother, still cryed he, vntill such time as she per-
ceiued his place of abiding, where (no doubt) but
*Tom* was in a pitifull taking, but the poore Cow in a
farre worse, hauing such a nimble timberd fellow
dancing Trench-more in her belly. But to conclude,
the poore beast could not be deliuered of her trou-
blesome burthen, till a laxatiue drinke cast into her
belley, had turned him out in a Cowturd. Who all
besmeared as he was, went home with his mother to
be made cleane. This was another of *Tom Thumbes*
most dangerous aduentures, which he most happily
escaped.

---

2 a-milking] a milking L.        10 leafe.] leafe L.
17 *Turned* m *in* much L.        18 Kine,] *probable reading; repair in volume.*
21 mother,] mother L.        31 happily] hapyily L.

How *Tom Thumbe*, in stead of a wheat corne,
was carried away in a Rauens
mouth.

*A*Nother time *Tom Thumbe*, being desirous to
helpe his Father driue the plowe, and in seedes-
time to see the manner of his sowing wheate, the
which the olde | man agreed to, and taking his     [B2
litle sonne vp, he put him into his pocket, and being
come to the field where his land lay, he set *Tom* in
one of his horses eares, and so droue all the rest
round about the Land, as if hee had gone by their
sides, so propper, so fine, and so nimble a light fellow was this *Tom Thumbe*, that the horses eare serued for a shelter to keepe him from raine and foule
weather, and likewise preserued him as well from
drowning in a beasts footestep, as from the windes
blowing him away, and many times from loosing
himselfe in Chaffe and Prouender, where surely he
had beene eaten vp amongst horses: but yet for all
these great cares thus taken by his Father, another
most strange and dangerous euent behapped him,
for as his father went a-sowing wheat vp and down
the land, *Tom Thumbe* was appointed to scarre away
Crowes, who with a cudgell made of a Barley straw,
for that purpose, stood most manfully in the middle
of the land, crying, Shooe, shooe, Crow, shooe; but
amongst the rest, there came a huge blacke Rauen,
that in stead of a wheate corne, carried poore *Tom*
quite away, where he was not of a long time heard

3 *Thumbe*,] *Tumbe*, L.     7 Turned *m* in *Thumbe* L.
25 a-sowing] a sowing L.

of, either by Fa- | ther or Mother: which great
losse of this their little Son they long time after-
ward mourned for, with many a sad and heauy la-
mentation, spending whole dayes and weekes, and
weary iourneys in seeking him vp and downe, but
all in vaine; there was not a Crowes nest in a whole
countrey but they searched, nor a Church steeple
within ten miles, nor a Pidgeon-hole but they
looked into, nor a Counterpit amongst boyes, nor
hardly a cherrypit was forgotten: but all lost labour, *Tom* was not to be found, but vtterly lost and
gone for euer, without al hope of recouery to be got
againe; whose want (as I said before) bred in his old
Parents hearts most heauy and long lamentations:
where wee will leaue them now mourning, and tell
of their lost litle sonnes succeeding fortunes and aduentures.

How *Tom Thumbe* fell in at a Chimney
top, and what happened to
him there.

*TOm Thumbe*, being thus taken vp by a Rauen (as
you heard) in stead of a graine of wheat, was
carried in her beake | ouer a great forrest, where in  [B3
all the way of this her long flight, *Tom Thumbe* did
nothing but cry, Shough, shough Crowe, shough,
in this maner affrighting the poore Rauen in her
flight, that she durst neither swallow him downe
her maw, nor let him fall out of her beake, vntill
such time, as what with faintnesse in flying, or al-

most starued with hunger, being quite tyred with
this her heauy burthen and long iourney, she was
constrained to rest on the top of an olde Castle wall
moted round about with an exceeding deepe riuer,
which belonged to an ancient and neuer conquered
Giant, that onely there inhabited without any
other company: This Rauen (as I said) resting on
the top of the Castle, and being ouerwearied, *Tom
Thumbe* with a nimble skip suddenly escaped both
from her beake and tallons, and with much lightnesse leapt vp to the top of the Castle chimney,
where being set, and looking downe, he espied the
Gyant sitting by his fire, boyling, broyling and
roasting the ioynts and quarters of men, deuouring
them all one after another, legs, armes and heads
bit by bit till they were all eaten vp at last: which
fearful sight so amazed *Tom Thumbe*, that he knew
not what to | doe, nor tell how to get away; to   [B3ᵛ]
escape was impossible: for the Castle wall was too
high for him to get downe, and the riuer too deepe
for such a little fellowe to wade ouer: so, being in
these fearefull and dangerous doubts, of a sodaine
came a puffe of winde, and blew poore *Tom* downe
into the Gyants Chimney, where he grew almost
besides his wits, to see himselfe by the fire side:
whom when the Gyant saw, thinking him to be
some Fairy, or a spirit come thither by miracle, ran
with an eager fury to catch him; but so nimble and
quicke was this little fellowe, that the Gyant had
no feeling of him, for when he caught him in his
hand, hee slipt out betweene his fingers, and being
in his armes, he crept out betweene his elbowes; so

---

15 legs,] legs L.    26 *Space but no comma after* saw L.
30 caught] canght L.    32 out] ont L.

that neither strength nor policy could take him.
Thus for that time escaped little *Tom*, where for his
more securitie, he crept into a mouse-hole, and there
safely for that night slept hee freely from the
Gyants intended cruelty. |

### How *Tom Thumbe* became the Gyants man, and what happened to him in that seruice.

*Tom Thumbe* being thus safe in lodging, (I meane
in the Mouse hole) put the Gyant in a great
wonder, maruelling what was become of him, for
which cause hee went supperlesse to bed, but could
not sleepe all that night following for thinking of
*Tom Thumbe*, which he deemed to bee some strange
creature, in that he had so nimbly escaped his
clutches: therefore in the middle of the night, hee
rose vp and tooke his clubbe, (which was the whole
arme of an Oke) and went vp and downe the Castle
in the darke, (for light had he none) crying with a
roaring voyce, in this maner following,

> *Now fi, fee, fau, fan,*
> *I feele smell of a dangerous man:*
> *Be he aliue, or be he dead,*
> *Ile grind his bones to make me bread.*

These fearefull speeches, thus thundred out by
this Gyant, put poore *Tom* into a | pittifull taking
not knowing what to doe, nor how to behaue him-

selfe; yet at last considered, it was but misery to be
thus imprisoned in this litle closet of darknesse, and
thought it better (then to lye there) to aduenture
foorth and submit himselfe to the Gyants mercy,
which most willingly he accepted of, and employed
this his new litle man, about his houshold businesse: wherevpon *Tom* became very diligent and
seruiceable: for the Gyant had no other Cat to catch
Mise and Rats, but *Tom;* no other broome to sweepe
10 cobwebs from any corner of his house but *Tom;* no
other key to open his lockes, but *Tom;* so *Tom* was
very fitting and nimble for any businesse whatso-
euer. But now marke the euent: the Gyant on a time
had a litle roastmeat to be laid to the fire, and *Tom*
must be the turn-spit: whereupon, sitting in the
Chimney-corner vpon a litle chip of wood to turne
the spit, holding a spoone before him to keepe the
heate from his face, (for indeede the spoone couered
his whole body) the Gyant now thinking to take
20 *Tom* at the aduantage, and to know whether hee
was a humane creature, or a spirit, of a sudden
catched at *Tom*, purposing to grinde the poore fel-
lowes bones and | body into pieces; but *Tom* hauing    [B5
more then an ordinary nimblenesse in himselfe, did,
(when the Gyant tooke hold of him) giue a skippe
downe (vnchewed) into his throat, and so into his
belly, and there kept such a rumbling and tumbling
in his guts, as if hee would haue gnawne a hole
quite thorow: it little booted the Gyant to rest in
30 quiet, for he thought the Diuell or his dam had
plaide at Tennis in his paunch: therefore in a fury
hyed he vp to the toppe of his Castle wall, where he

disgorged his stomacke, and cast out his burthen,
at least three miles into the Sea, (vpon the bankes
whereof this Castle stood) where *Tom Thumbe* was
most brauely entertained by a Fishe, which swal-
lowed him downe aliue, in which watry dwelling
he remained, till the same Fishe was taken, and
giuen for a present to King *Arthurs* Table, where this
noble and aduenturous little Gallant was found, and
for the strangenesse of his stature, accepted of for
10 his Highnesse Dwarfe, and so by this means *Tom
Thumbe* became a Courtier. |

[B5ᵛ

## Of *Tom Thumbes* behauiour in Court, and
## the honours by him atchie-
## ued there.

*T*Om Thumbe* being now in Court, became a com-
panion for Ladies and Gentlewomen, and so
20 braue minded that not any in King *Arthurs* Palace
gained more fauours then hee did, insomuch that
the Ladies and Gentlewomen could seldome bee
without him; for his company was so pleasing, that
many times they gaue him leaue to sleepe vpon their
knees, and now and then in their pockets, with
many such like priuate places, and withall to sit
vpon their pinpillowes, and play with their pinnes,
and to runne at tilt against their bosomes with a bul-
rush; for bigger weapon was hee not able to man-
30 age. But now marke what happened: vpon a time
King *Arthur* appointed a royall triumph in his
Court, with great reuelling and masking to be

holden amongst his Knights, where Sir *Lancelot-
du-Lake*, Sir *Triamor*, and Sir *Tristram*, all of the
round Table, performed many noble acts | of   [B6
Cheualry: amongst which worthy Gallants, *Tom
Thumbe* would not sit out, and being then in great
fauour, to his vtmost skill, would approue himselfe
a right Courtier; whereupon, amongst them all, in
presence of the King, Queene, and others of the
Nobilitie, hee requested one of the Maydes of Hon-
10  our to hold foorth her hand, where, vpon the Palme
thereof he daunced a most excellent Galliard, to the
wonderfull and great admiration of all the behold-
ers; for which noble performance, were many rich
guifts bestowed vpon him, as well by strangers as
Peeres of the Land; amongst the rest, the King himselfe gaue him a gold Ring from his owne finger, the
which *Tom Thumbe* wore for a girdle, as a fauour
about his middle, for it was the iust compasse of his
body to hoope it in round.
20

---

How *Tom Thumbe* grew daily into more
fauour with the King, and of a boone
obtained of his Highnesse.

*K*Ing *Arthur* seldome sate amongst his Knights of
the round Table, but | *Tom Thumbe* was in   [B6ᵛ
company, either amongst their spangled feathers, or
sitting vpon the pommel of the Kings own chaire,
30  such great delight had his Highnesse in his company, that he seldome rode abroad, but *Tom* was
cockered vpon his saddle-bow, where alwaies when

---

6 himselfe] himseife L.        7 them] rhem L.
28 spangled] spaugled L.

it rained, would he creepe in at a button-hole of the
Kings doublet to keepe himselfe dry; where being
settled so neere his Highnesse heart, that he con-
tinually obtained what hee asked for, and now
hauing opportunity fitting to beg a boone, and
withall remembring his old father and mother,
whom he had not of a long time seene, he requested
of the King to giue him a burthen of money, no
more then his backe could carry, from his Treasury,
therewithal to relieue his father and mother in their
old dayes: which request no sooner obtained, but
away goes *Tom Thumbe*, and loades himselfe with a
burthen of money from the Kings Treasury, which
was in all, no more but a poore three-pence, the
whole waight that his body could carry at one
time: so trauelling two dayes and two nights, with
long labour, he gat some thirty yardes from King
*Arthurs* Court, some part of the way towards his
Fathers | house, that being all the iourney he was            [B7
able to goe in fourty eight houres, bearing so huge
and heauy a burthen vppon his shoulders: so from
time to time, and from iourney to iourney, he came
at last (though with great wearinesse) to his
Fathers doore, not in all distant from King *Arthurs*
Pallace, aboue three quarters of a mile; whom when
his Father and Mother beheld, for very ioy they
swouned; but recouering themselues, his Mother
tooke him vp in her handkercher for feare of hurt-
ing his bones, and carried him into the great hall,
where she set him in a Wal-nut-shell (in stead of a
chaire) by a good fire to warme himselfe. Where
after a litle refreshing, and much reioycing, hee de-

liuered vp the great masse of treasure giuen him by
King *Arthur*, which hee had brought with such long
iournies, and great paines to his father and mother.
The money receiued, they got him to supper, where
the cloath was laid vpon his mothers hand, and the
seruice was the curnell of a hazell-nut, of which he
eate but the third part, and the rest serued him suf-
ficiently for foure meales after, yet grew he some-
times sicke by eating so much at one time. |

10     Thus after that *Tom Thumbe*, with his Father and   [B7ᵛ
Mother, had ryoted for certaine moneths, Time
called him away to his charge in Court: but not
knowing how to get thither, by reason of a great
Flood that was risen by a few Aprill drops, hee
grewe into a very great melancholly, and made
most heauy lamentations. Whereupon his Father
hauing a ready, and quicke fore-casting wit, but a
farre stronger breath, tooke a birding trunke of
Wood, and put his sonne *Thomas* therein, and at one
20 blast: blew him into King *Arthurs* Court: Where
(after this his great iourney) hee was entertained
with Triumphs and much Reuelling.

---

Of the gifts that the Queene of Fayries gaue her god-sonne: and of
the rare and excellent ver-
tues thereof.

30 *TOm Thumbes* renowne and honours, growing to
the full height of Fame in this Kingdome, caused
people to come from all parts of the Land to visit

---

11. moneths,] moneths. L.     16. heavy] heauy L.
17. fore-casting] fore casting L.

him: some with one present, some with another, |
to bestow vpon him. Amongst the rest, his olde   [B8
Godmother the Queene of Fayries came for to see
him, and to witnesse what Fame and good Fortunes
had befallen him.

But so it happened, that she found her little God-
sonne asleepe (in the Kings Garden) vpon the toppe
of a Red Rose new blowne. And being then iust
highnoone-tide, (her chiefest time of liberty to
10 worke wonders in) she stood inuisibly before him,
stroaking downe the sweaty droppes with her
vnfelt hand from his little forehead, which cast him
into a most sweete and pleasurable dreame, and
withall bestowed foure of the most rarest guifts of
the world vpon him, which she left there lying by
against his awaking. First, an inchanted Hat, the
which by wearing hee should know, what was done
in all parts of the world. A Ring likewise inchanted,
that hauing it vpon his finger, hee might goe if hee
20 pleased into any place vnseene, and walke inuisible.
Thirdly, a Girdle, that by wearing it, should
change him into what shape soeuer he desired. And
lastly, a payre of shooes, (that being on his feete)
would in a moment carry him to any part | of the   [B8ᵛ
earth, and to be any time where hee pleased. Thus
with a feruency of loue blessed shee him, and departed. Whereupon *Tom Thumbe* awaked, as out of a
golden slumber, and found these aforesaid guifts as
his good Godmother had left him, the which being
30 well considered of, (and as it was reuealed to him in
his sleepe) he first tooke the Hat and put it vpon his
head: wherupon he was presently inspired with the

---

11. droppes] droppes) L.          28. aforesaid] asoresaid L.

knowledge of al things in the world; and at that
very instant knew, what was done in K. *Arthurs*
Court, and what the King himself was a doing.
Next, putting on the ring, he went as he wished
inuisible, and caught birds as they sate in bushes:
fowles in the ayre, and such like. Then putting on
the Girdle, hee wisht himselfe a Gyant, then a
Dwarfe, then a fish, then a worme, then a man, &c.
Lastly, putting on the Shooes, which no sooner on
10  his feete, but he was carried as quicke as thought
into another world, where hee sawe wonders, as
men without heads, their faces on their breasts,
some with one legge, some with one eye in the forehead, some of one shape, some of another: then by
and by was he come backe againe into King *Arthurs*
Court. |

_____  [C1

20      How *Tom Thumbe* riding forth to take the
          ayre, met with the great *Garagantua,*
                and of the speach that was
                        betweene them.

*T*'*Om Thumbe* on a time being weary, crept into a
      Ladies pocket, and there rested himselfe, this
Lady forgetting of her seruant *Thomas,* suddenly
pulled foorth her handkercher, and with her handkercher *Tom Thumbe:* she blowing her nose with it
30  so frighted poore *Thomas,* that the little Gentleman
fell in a sownd, but they fetched him againe with
the hundred part of an Aquauity drop: yet for all

_____

6. putting] pntting L.

their care that they tooke hee was troubled with a
great Palsie, and none of the Kings Physitions could
cure him. The King grieued to see his little Gentleman in this taking, and for his recouery spared no
cost, for he sent for the chiefe Physition to King
*Twaddell*, which was King of the Pigmies, (which
King and his subiects are but two foote high from
the ground,) this Physition being litle of body, but
great of skill, soone found out his disease and cured
him. |                                              [C1ᵛ]

    *Tom Thumbe* being cured rod foorth in his Coach
one day to take the ayre, his Coach was made of
halfe a Wal-nut-shell, the wheeles were made of
foure button-mouldes, and foure blew flesh-flyes
drewe it: Riding in this maner by the Wood side he
chanced to meete the great *Garagantua*, who was
riding also to solace himselfe, his horse being of
that great bignesse, as is described in the booke of
his honourable deedes, and himselfe being in height
not inferiour to any steeple. *Tom Thumbe* seeing of
him, asked what he was? *Garagantua* answered him,
that he was the onely wonder of the world, the
terror of the people, and the tamer of man and beast:
stay there said *Tom Thumbe*, for I am to be wondred
at as much as thy selfe any waies can bee: for I am
not onely feared, but also loued: I cannot onely
tame men and beastes, but I also can tame thy selfe.
Hereat *Garagantua* fell into such a laughter that the
whole earth where hee stood shooke which made
*Tom Thumbe* in all hast to ride away, and to beate
his winged steades into a false Gallop.

---

20. steeple.] steeple L.      27. selfe.] selfe L.
31. winged] winged L.

*Garagantua* seeing him in this feare desired him to
stay, and they would talke fa- | miliarly, who was    [C2
the better man, and could doe the most wonders.
Hereto *Tom Thumbe* consented, and caused his
Coach to stand, and they began to dispute dialogue
maner as followeth. Dwarfe, quoth *Garagantua*, I
can blow downe a Steeple with my breath, I can
drowne a whole Towne with my pisse, I can eate
more then a hundred, I drinke more then a hundred,
10   I carry more then a hundred, I can kill more then a
hundred: all this can I do, now tell what thou canst
doe?

I can doe more then this, saide *Tom Thumbe*, for I
can creepe into a keyhole, and see what any man or
woman doe in their priuate chambers, there I see
things that thou art not worthy to know. I can saile
in an egge-shel, which thou canst not: I can eate
lesse then a Wren, and so saue victuals: I can drinke
lesse then a Sparrow, therefore I am no drunkard: I
20   cannot kill a Rat with my strength, and therefore
am no murtherer: these qualities of mine are better
then thine in all mens iudgements, and therefore
great monster I am thy better.

Hereat *Garagantua* was madde and would with
his foote haue kicked downe | the whole wood,    [C2ᵛ
and so haue buried *Tom Thumbe: Tom* seeing of it,
with his skill so inchanted him that he was not able
to stur, but so stood still with one leg vp, till *Tom
Thumbe* was at his lodging: Hereat *Garagantua*
30   was much vexed, but knew not how to helpe himselfe.

---

6. *Garagantua*] *Garagantuta* L.

How *Tom Thumbe* after conference had with
great *Garagantua* returned, and how he
met with King *Twadle*.

*T*Om Thumbe* being somewhat well at ease by taking of the fresh aire returned backe againe to the
Court of King *Arthur*, who no sooner being come,
but great preparation was made for the entertaine-
ment of so tall a person, as that the officers of the
house with all their seruants were in a sweat to
prouide for this tall Sir *Thomas Thumbe* his dinner.

This entertainment being ended, K. *Arthur* sent
for *Tom Thumbe*, and being come, withdrew themselues into a priuate roome, where *Tom* told King
*Arthur* what strang | accidents befell to him in    [C3
meeting of great *Garagantua*, and of their conference
together; as likewise of their exploits: and after-
ward how by his skill he enchanted him in the
wood where they met, and there left him: whereat
K. *Arthur* was wonderfully amazed, hearing of the
strength of that mighty Gyant *Garagantua*.

Then he told K. *Arthur* how he met with K.
*Twadle* being King of the Pigmes, a man of mighty
stature in comparison of *Tom Thumbe*, being not two
foote high, this stout King did he ouerthrow at
Tilt both horse and man: and all these things did he
performe by vertue that was in the guifts which his
godmother the Queene of Fairies did bestow vpon
her godsonne *Tom Thumb:* which was his Hat of
knowledge, his Ring which made him goe inuisible,

his Girdle which made him bee what he wisht to be
either man or beast, and lastly his shooes, which
being on his feet was on a sudden in any part of the
world, and in the twinkling of an eye was in King
*Arthurs* Court againe.

Where wee will now leaue this little wonderous
Gentleman of all ages, with these his most precious
Reliques of ad- | miration, and so ending this first [C3ᵛ
part of our ancient story of Sir *Thomas Thumbe:*
where if it like the Reader, the second
part shall be followed with tales
of more maruell, by the
Author hereof.

*R. I.*


FINIS.

# The Renaissance English Text Society

## Council

PRESIDENT, Ernest Sirluck, *University of Toronto*
VICE-PRESIDENT, W. A. Jackson, *Harvard University*
SECRETARY, Samuel Schoenbaum, *Northwestern University*
TREASURER, Louis L. Martz, *228 Hall of Graduate Studies, Yale University, New Haven, Connecticut*
Gerald E. Bentley, *Princeton University*
Fredson T. Bowers, *University of Virginia*
Hugh G. Dick, *University of California at Los Angeles*
G. Blakemore Evans, *University of Illinois*
J. G. McManaway, *Folger Shakespeare Library*

CORRESPONDING SECRETARY-TREASURER FOR U. K. AND EUROPE
T. S. Dorsch, *Westfield College, University of London, London, N. W. 3*

The Renaissance English Text Society was founded to publish scarce literary texts, chiefly non-dramatic, of the period 1475–1660. Normally two volumes a year will be distributed to subscribing members. Members may purchase additional copies, and new members may buy previous publications of the Society while supplies last. Membership is open without election to interested individuals and institutions. The annual subscription within the United States and Canada is ten dollars, and in the United Kingdom and the rest of the sterling area two pounds ten shillings. Dollar subscriptions should be sent to the Treasurer, Louis L. Martz, sterling subscriptions to the Corresponding Secretary-Treasurer, T. S. Dorsch.

THE
UNIVERSITY OF WINNIPEG
PORTAGE & BALMORAL
WINNIPEG 2, MAN.    CANADA